A MEDICAL
GREEK AND LATIN
WORKBOOK

A MEDICAL GREEK AND LATIN WORKBOOK

SECOND EDITION

By

JAMES A. McCULLOCH, Ph. D.

Professor of Classics
Dean, College of Liberal Arts & Sciences
Duquesne University
Pittsburgh, Pennsylvania

Foreword by

John G. Adams, Ph.D.

Vice President
Scientific & Professional Relations
Pharmaceutical Manufacturers Association
Washington, D.C.

CHARLES   C   THOMAS   •   PUBLISHER
Springfield • Illinois • U.S.A.

Published and Distributed Throughout the World by
CHARLES C THOMAS • PUBLISHER
2600 South First Street
Springfield, Illinois 62717

© *1962 and 1984 by* CHARLES C THOMAS • PUBLISHER

ISBN 0-398-04905-X

Library of Congress Catalog Card Number: 83-9188

First Edition, First Printing, 1962
First Edition, Second Printing, 1970
First Edition, Third Printing, 1974
First Edition, Fourth Printing, 1977
Second Edition, 1984

Printed in the United States of America
Q-R-1

Library of Congress Cataloging in Publication Data

McCulloch, James A.
    A medical Greek and Latin workbook.

    Bibliography: p.
    1.   Medicine--Terminology.   2.   Greek
language--Medical Greek.   3. Latin language--Medical
Latin.   I. Title. [DNLM: 1. Nomenclature.
W 15 M133m]
R123.M36   1984   610'.1'4   83-9188
ISBN 0-398-04905-X

Foreword

All learning, whether it be in the sciences or humanities, is dependent upon language for the communication of facts and ideas. J. Willard Gibbs, in one of his rare public statements, emphatically stated that "Mathematics is a language!" and indeed it is, as any student familiar with symbolology of the subject is well aware. Any system used to communicate information is a language and though the symbolology of mathematics is a very special case in point, it emphasizes the importance of language as a tool for the transmission and interpretation of information.

Each academic discipline or area of knowledge possesses its own idiosyncrasies of language, if in no other aspect than in the vocabulary or symbols, as the case may be. Inadequate vocabulary is a serious impediment to communication and learning as any teacher knows from experience in the classroom. The development of vocabulary and the ability to utilize a knowledge of words to convey ideas clearly and unambiguously is the *sine qua non* of education in any field.

The language of science is probably best understood and communicated by the student or teacher who has an appreciation of and an interest in the "science of language." Semantics is a prerequisite for comprehension of ideas and it follows that etymology, as a branch of semantics, should not be neglected as a tool for learning.

The development of a scientific vocabulary is generally accomplished in several ways. There is no easy approach. The most frequent method is learning by rote without regard to etymology or context. Quite apart from the time necessary and the limitations imposed by the individual student's capacity for memorization and retention, this method leads to the false assumption that if terms are defined or understood, the principle is likewise understood. Contextual definition eliminates the latter criticism of memory exercises in the definition of scientific words or terms, but, unless the student is familiar with antecedent and subsequent words, terms, or phrases of a given passage, the method falls short of providing the means for clear definition and understanding. Etymological definition, though dependent on memorization of prefixes, suffixes, and roots, offers the distinct advantage of grouping and classifying information. In scanning a scientific or medical dictionary, one is immediately aware of the frequent occurrence of common prefixes, suffixes, and roots which form the basis of countless words in scientific language. And it is an established fact that knowledge of them provides a rational and expedient approach to the development of a scientific vocabulary.

In an age when the study of the classical languages has been de-emphasized, a reference source of common prefixes, suffixes, and roots is of definite value to the student of science. The present volume, in addition to providing a source of these word elements, incorporates the very important aspect of practice in their use. *A Medical Greek and Latin Workbook* is both a lexicon and primer and lends itself admirably to use in formalized courses in etymology or disciplines in which new and unfamiliar terms are introduced. The availability of this volume is a distinct contribution to a fuller and richer appreciation of the language of science and scientists.

JOHN G. ADAMS, PH.D.

Washington, D.C.

Preface to Second Edition

The use of Greek and Latin for medical terminology has obvious advantages over the use of modern languages. Because both are dead languages, the meanings of words never change. It is, therefore, easy to coin new words to describe new medical concepts. Since the first edition of this work, the number of medical terms has increased dramatically, and almost all of the new words have been created from Greek and Latin. Thus, inasmuch as Greek and Latin do not add words to their vocabularies and the meanings of words do not change, medical terminology can be expanded infinitely by using the ancient languages.

The general pattern of the previous edition has been retained in the preparation of this revision. Exercises have been expanded and new lessons added, as well as English-Greek and English-Latin vocabularies. The revisions provide for well over three hundred words not found in the previous edition.

I especially wish to express my appreciation to my assistant Janice Grey, whose devotion to preparing the manuscript for publication made my task pleasant. In addition to her careful and painstaking editorial effort, she compiled the English-Greek and English-Latin vocabularies, which will prove helpful to those students using this book. My thanks also go to Professor Henry C. Schoming, C.S.Sp., for his valuable suggestions for revisions of the text.

JAMES A. McCULLOCH

Pittsburgh, Pennsylvania

Preface to First Edition

This book furnishes information relating to the origin of words and provides exercises designed to cultivate and increase the word power of students pursuing medical and paramedical careers. To reach this goal the plan is to present a variety of disciplinary lessons which will oblige the student to employ basic principles of word origin leading to the expansion of his vocabulary.

Undergraduate college students, and even graduate school candidates, encounter great difficulty in many of their courses of study when they are confronted with a vast array of new words and terms. All too often they find that the terminology of one branch of learning seems to be foreign and inapplicable to another area of study. Hence, a great deal of time is spent laboriously learning definitions and memorizing individual terms with no awareness of their origin or general significance. Since the major flow of medical terminology springs from the fountainheads of Greek and Latin, adequate preparation in the classical languages would help eliminate this problem. But unfortunately, to the detriment of students, classical education is scantily offered or absent from the high school curriculum.

In order to alleviate this condition, and thereby increase the vocabulary of students, this workbook contains Greek and Latin prefixes, words, and suffixes which the student is most likely to encounter during his years of study in both the preprofessional and professional curricula. The material is presented in such a way that no previous knowledge of the Greek or Latin language is prerequisite.

The enlargement of the student's total vocabulary is the ultimate objective of this book. Its immediate objectives, however, are: (1) to increase the student's scientific vocabulary through a better understanding of the component parts of English words derived from Greek and Latin; (2) to enable the student, through a basic knowledge of etymology, to decipher, analyze and deduce the meanings of scientific as well as nonscientific words he meets in his reading and study; and (3) to improve his pronunciation and spelling.

To achieve these objectives an ample number of exercises and review lessons are included in the text to give the student an immediate facility in determining the derivation of words, their scientific meaning, spelling and pronunciation.   In the performance of these exercises it is highly desirable that the student have ready access to a Webster's unabridged dictionary, a standard medical dictionary and one or more source-books, such as Jaeger, E. C.: *Source-Book of Medical Terms* (Springfield, Charles C Thomas, Publisher, 1953). A number of other dictionaries and reference books may be found in the bibliography.

Blank sheets for notes are included opposite each lesson.   These note sheets are provided for the student's convenience in recording any questions he may have on any particular word or words he meets while working independently outside of class.   They are also to be used for the taking of classroom' notes pertinent to the adjacent lesson.   The teacher, as well as the student, may advantageously use this welcome space for inserting accessory roots and words in addition to those listed.

The book is divided into two parts.   Part One is devoted to words of Greek origin, while Part Two treats words of Latin origin. At the end of each part there is a review lesson for test purposes. These review lessons are intended to serve also as a sample format for additional tests which the instructor, at his discretion, may wish to use.

The vocabularies in both parts are formed from word lists supplied by colleagues in the basic and professional science courses. Categorization of terms into exclusive packets pertaining to anatomy, pathology, bacteriology and so on has been deliberately avoided.   Emphasis throughout the manual is placed upon constant repetition of prefixes, stems, combining forms, and suffixes in variant word combinations.   From repetition of etymological definitions illustrating basic principles involved in the origin of words flow the comprehension and retention of words and their meanings.

The final form of this workbook has been developed, formulated and organized after use in actual classroom sessions. Diligent study of the book will increase the student's vocabulary, and, even more important, his broadened use of this enlarged vocabulary will reward him with better understanding of the ideas and concepts in scientific, cultural and professional courses.

JAMES A. MCCULLOCH

Pittsburgh, Pennsylvania

Abbreviations

adj. . . . . adjective
adv . . . . .adverb
c . . . . .common
comb. form . . . . .combining form
comp. adj. . . . . .comparative adjective
conj . . . . .conjunction
dim . . . . .diminutive
f. . . . . .feminine noun
gen . . . . .genitive case
m . . . . .masculine noun
n . . . . .neuter noun
n . . . . .noun
nom . . . . .nominative case
num . . . . .numeral
pl . . . . .plural
pp. . . . . .perfect passive participle
prep . . . . .preposition
pron . . . . .pronoun
sing . . . . .singular
sup. adj . . . . .superlative adjective
v . . . . .verb

Note: *or* between two forms of a word indicates that both forms are found, e.g., **femur, -oris** *or* **-inis.**

Contents

A MEDICAL
GREEK AND LATIN
WORKBOOK

Part One

MEDICAL GREEK

Medical Greek

1. The Greek Alphabet

The Greek alphabet has twenty-four letters:

Character	Name	Transliteration	Sound
α	alpha	a	dr*a*ma
β	beta	b	*b*et
γ	gamma	g, ng (hard)	*g*o, gan*g*
δ	delta	d	*d*o
ε	epsilon	e (short)	s*e*t
ζ	zeta	z	*z*one
η	eta	e (long)	th*ey*
θ	theta	th	*th*ing
ι	iota	i	s*i*t, mach*i*ne
κ	kappa	k, c	*k*ill
λ	lambda	l	*l*ong
μ	mu	m	*m*ay
ν	nu	n	*n*ot
ξ	xi	x	la*x*
o	omicron	o (short)	*o*bey
π	pi	p	*p*ut
ρ	rho	r, rh	*r*ow
σ, s	sigma	s	*s*ip
τ	tau	t	*t*ip
υ	upsilon	y, u	French *u*
φ	phi	ph	*Ph*ilip
χ	chi	ch	lo*ch* (Scotch)
ψ	psi	ps	li*ps*
ω	omega	o (long)	*s*o

Note

(a) γ becomes *n* before κ, γ, χ, or ξ when transliterated: φάρυγξ = pharynx.

(b) There are two signs for sigma. The form s is used only as a final letter, the form σ everywhere else: σύστασις.

(c) ρ at the beginning of a word becomes *rh:* ῥίς = rhis. When an initial ρ is preceded by a prefix or an element which ends in a vowel, the letter is usually doubled, but remains single after a diphthong: διά-ρροια = diarrhea; εὐ-ρυθμία = eurythmy.

5

2. Breathings

The *h* sound is indicated by a rough breathing ('). This symbol, which indicates aspiration of a vowel, is placed above an initial vowel or over the second vowel of an initial diphthong: ἕξις = hexis. A smooth breathing (') is placed over all unaspirated initial vowels and diphthongs: ἄλγος = algos.

3. Vowels

The vowels are α, ε, η, ι, o, υ, and ω. The vowels η and ω are always long: ε and o are always short; α, ι, and υ are either long or short depending upon the word in which they appear.

4. Diphthongs

αι becomes ae or e:	αἰθήρ	= aether or ether.
αυ becomes au:	τραῦμα	= trauma.
ει becomes ei or i:	χειράγρα	= cheiragra or chiragra.
ευ becomes eu:	εὔνοια	= eunoia.
οι becomes oe or e:	ἀμοιβή	= amoeba or ameba.
ου becomes ou or u:	οὐλῖτις	= oulitis or ulitis.

5. Accents

There are three accents in Greek, acute (´), grave (`), and circumflex (^). These will not be considered in the pronunciation of scientific Greek inasmuch as we generally follow the Latin rules for accentuation. In Latin, words of two syllables are accented on the penult. In words of three or more syllables, the accent falls upon the penult, if it is long, otherwise on the antepenult. A syllable is long if it contains a long vowel or a diphthong, or if the vowel is followed by two consonants or by *x* or *z*.

COMBINING TECHNIQUES

6. Greek Nouns

Greek nouns are inflected in three declensions. The connective vowel o is generally added to the base of the Greek noun to make a combining form for compound words.

(a) **First or A-Declension nouns** have nominative endings of **-a, -as, -e, -es.** The base is found by dropping these endings:

Noun	Meaning	Base	Combining form	Example
glossa	tongue	gloss	glosso-	glossotomy
odyne	pain	odyn	odyno-	odynophobia

(b) **Second or O-Declension nouns** end in **-os,** or **-on.** By dropping these endings the base is found:

Noun	Meaning	Base	Combining form	Example
nephros	kidney	nephr	nephro-	nephropathy
neuron	nerve	neur	neuro-	neurocyte

(c) **Third or Consonant Declension nouns** have various endings in the nominative singular case. The base of third declension nouns is generally found by removing the genitive singular ending **-os** or **-eos:**

Noun	Meaning	Base	Combining form	Example
pous, podos	foot	pod	podo-	podology
is, inos	fiber	in	ino-	inolith
plexis, plexeos	stroke	plex	plexo-	plexalgia

7. Greek Adjectives

Adjectives are inflected like nouns. To make the combining form add the connective vowel **o** to the base. However, Greek adjectives ending in **-ys** in the nominative singular, as **polys,** often take the combining form from the nominative singular by simply dropping the final **s,** as **poly-**.

8. Greek Verbs

The bases and combining forms of Greek verbs are so numerous that no simple rule can be given as a guide.

9. Greek Prefixes

Prefix	Meaning	Example
a-, an- (before vowels)	without, lack of, negation	*apod*
amphi-, ampho-	about, around, on both sides	*amphitheater*
ana-	up, upon, apart, throughout	*analysis*
anti-	against	*antinomy*

apo-, ap-, aph-	away, from	*apogee*
cata-	down, under	*catabasis*
dia-	through, apart	*diarrhea*
dys-	bad, faulty, painful	*dysentery*
ec-	out of, from	*eccentric*
ecto-, ect-	outside	*ectoderm*
en-, em-	in	*endermic*
endo-, ento-	within	*endogeny*
epi-, ep-, eph-	on, upon	*epidermic*
eso-	inward, within	*esogastritis*
eu-	well, good, easy	*euphony*
exo-	outside, without	*exogamy*
hemi-	half	*hemisphere*
hyper-	over, above, beyond, excessive	*hyperbola*
hypo-, hyp-	below, under, deficient	*hypothesis*
meta, met-, meth-	after, beyond, change	*metamorphic*
para-, par-	beside, near, abnormal	*parasite*
peri-	around, near	*perimeter*
pro-	before	*prognosis*
pros-	to, before, near	*prosencephalon*
syn-, sym-	together, with	*sympathy*

10. Greek Suffixes

Suffix	*Meaning*	*Example*
-ac	concerning or pertaining to	*cardiac*
-atic		*asthmatic*
-etic		*genetic*
-ic		*cephalic*
-itic		*arthritic*
-tic		*biotic*
-esis	state, condition, act, quality of	*enuresis*
-sis		*diagnosis*
-ia		*anemia*
-y		*agony*
-gen	producing	*carcinogen*
-osis	disease, increase of, state of	*nephrosis*
-iasis		*psoriasis*
		leucocytosis
-ism	state, condition, belief, doctrine	*metabolism*
		theism
-ics	art or science of	*eugenics*
-ist	agent, one who practices, professes, or is skilled in	*biologist*
-itis	inflammation	*nephritis*
-ize	make, do, practice, change	*energize*
-oid	like, having the shape of	*spheroid*
-tery	place of	*cemetery*
-oma	tumor	*neuroma*

Notes:

LESSON I

11. Vocabulary

neuron, n.: nerve
algos, n.: pain
angeion, n.: vessel
cheir, cheiros, n.: hand
kranion, n.: the skull
pous, podos, n.: foot
nephros, n.: kidney
orthos, adj.: straight
pseudes, adj.: false, spurious
metron, n.: measure
gamos, n.: marriage
tachys, adj.: swift
lithos, n.: stone

grapho, v.: to write; the suffix *-graphy* often indicates a description or study of.
tomos, n.: a cutting; the suffix *-tome* often indicates the instrument for cutting.
bios, n.: life
isos, adj.: equal
mesos, adj.: middle
logos, n.: discourse, science
polys, adj.: many, much
tachos, n.: speed
trachelos, n.: throat, neck

12. Define etymologically:

chiralgia
craniamphitomy
nephrotomy
exogamy
diameter
nephrectomize
biologist
asymmetry
aneuria
isogamy
craniectomy
polygamy
isopod
neuric
biography

mesolithic
agraphia
biology
orthography
neuritis
podology
angiology
nephrolithiasis
chiropodalgia
neurectomy
pseudopod
nephralgia
mesonephros
neuroid
chiropodist

neuralgia
isodiametric
tachymeter
nephritis
apod
orthogamy
biometrics
atom
angiography
anatomy
biotic
perimeter
symbiosis
cranitis
mesoneuritis

13. Indicate the meaning suggested by the following Greek prefixes and suffixes:

1. dia-	2. syn-	3. eso-	4. apo-
5. hypo-	6. para-	7. anti-	8. a-
9. -oma	10. -ism	11. -ist	12. -ics
13. -oid	14. -ic	15. -y	16. -ia
17. -ac	18. -esis	19. -itis	20. -ize

Notes:

LESSON I

14. Using a standard medical dictionary, find the exact scientific meaning and indicate the pronunciation of each of the following words:

1. neuralgia	2. angiography	3. craniectomy
4. chiropodist	5. nephritis	6. pseudopod
7. mesoneuritis	8. anatomy	9. symbiosis

15. Transliterate into English these Greek Words:

1. νεῦρον	2. κύτος	3. σπόρος
4. λῆψις	5. ψώρα	6. μορφή
7. πούς	8. τροφή	9. κλόνος
10. θάλασσα	11. θρίξ	12. ἐρυθρός
13. ὦμος	14. τυρός	15. χεῖλος

16. List the prefixes which may be used to indicate the following meanings:

1. half	2. through	3. with
4. down	5. before	6. well
7. on both sides	8. without	9. against

17. List the suffixes which may be used to indicate the following meanings:

1. place of	2. disease	3. to make
4. inflammation	5. concerning	6. tumor
7. producing	8. like	9. agent

18. Indicate the base of these Greek words:

1. logos	2. polys	3. angeion
4. lapara	5. chole	6. omos
7. mesos	8. tachys	9. cheir

19. Accent the penult of the following words:

1. dactyl	2. hypochromic	3. eutrophic

Notes:

LESSON II

20. Vocabulary

phone, n.: sound, voice, tone
ge, n.: earth
arithmos, n.: number
arteria, n.: artery
arthron, n.: joint
sepsis, sepseos, n.: decay
aster, asteros, n.: star
astron, n.: star, constellation
sthenos, n.: strength
nomos, n.: law, custom
nekros, n.: dead body, corpse
phobia, n.: fear, fright
neos, adj.: new
homos, adj.: same

phyton, n.: plant
nosos, n.: disease
haima, haimatos, n.: blood
kytos, n.: cell
gala, galaktos, n.: milk
skleros, adj.: hard
gignomai (gen(e)-, gon-), v.: become, beget, produce
genesis, geneseos, n.: origin, descent, generation, production
rheos, n.: stream, current, flow
rheo, v.: to flow
erythros, adj.: red
heteros, adj.: other, different

21. Define etymologically:

neocytosis
nosography
neurasthenia
erythroneocytosis
erythrocytometer
phonometer
arthritic
geography
arteriotomy
nephrohemia
astrocytoma
necrophobia
necrosis
necrotomy
heterolith
homogametic

perigee
necrometer
neophyte
asthenia
galalith
galactoma
rheotome
nephrosclerosis
neocyte
nosology
arithmetic
phonophobia
apogee
geoid
necrobiosis
heterogenesis

nomogenesis
asthenic
rheometer
aphonic
geologist
neogala
arithmometer
arthritis
arthropod
astroid
metronome
heterophony
astronomy
sepsometer
astrophobia
nosohemia

22. Prepare a list of twenty derivatives especially useful to a student interested in biology. Use only standard reference books in the field of biological science. When the list is completed, consult an unabridged dictionary and show both the etymological and scientific meaning of each word on your list.

Notes:

LESSON II

23. Indicate the correct pronunciation of the following:

1. erythroneocytosis   2. nephrosclerosis   3. arteriotomy

24. State the exact scientific definition of each of the following medical terms:

1. nosohemia	2. necrosis	3. neocytosis
4. erythrocyte	5. arthritic	6. asthenia
7. nephrolithiasis	8. aneuria	9. trachelology

25. Transliterate the following Greek words into English:

1. λευκός	2. γένεσις	3. τόνος
4. σαπρός	5. στερεός	6. φλέψ
7. νεῦρον	8. λίθος	9. σπλήν
10. προσφυής	11. μηχανή	12. βλαστός

26. Indicate the meaning suggested by the following prefixes:

1. peri-	2. sym-	3. epi-	4. dys-
5. ana-	6. meta-	7. pro-	8. ecto-
9. para-	10. exo-	11. eso-	12. cata-

27. Indicate the base of these Greek words:

1. phone	2. gala	3. phyton
4. ouron	5. monos	6. kephale
7. erythros	8. aster	9. arithmos

28. Accent the antepenult of the following words:

1. euthymia   2. iridoplegia   3. nyctalgia

29. List two or more English derivatives from each of the following Greek words:

1. **nous, nou,** n.: the mind
2. **kryptos,** adj.: hidden
3. **spodos,** n.: ashes
4. **hieros,** adj.: holy

Notes:

LESSON III

30. Vocabulary

basis, baseos, n.: step, foundation
strobile, n.: twist of lint
thenar, thenaros, n.: palm of the hand
plexis, plexeos, n.: stroke
is, inos, n.: fiber, muscle
lordos, adj.: bent back
lapara, n.: flank, loin
dynamis, -eos and -ios, n.: power, force
penes, adj.: poor
hormao (hormon), v.: to excite
poikilos, adj.: varied
plethysmos, n.: enlargement, multiplication
ornis, ornithos, n.: bird

monos, adj.: one, alone, single
chorion, n.: skin
glykys, adj.: sweet; the combining form *glyco-* usually denotes sugar
ouron, n.: urine
broma, bromatos, n.: food
pharmakon, n.: drug, poison
apotheke, n.: storehouse
ateles, adj.: imperfect, incomplete
ektasis, -eos, n.: expansion, extension, stretching
lexis, lexeos, n.: word
oligos, adj.: few, little, small
mania, n.: madness
keimai, v.: to lie down
kolpos, n.: bosom (vagina)

31. Define etymologically:

nephrectasis
glycopenia
abasis
lordosis
monochorionic
pharmacy
pharmacophobia
atelopodia
monograph
inocyte
hormonogenesis
oligo-erythrocythemia
ornithosis
maniaphobia
oligogalactia
uro-erythrin
inogenesis
lordotic
orthocytosis
monomania
trachelectomy

pharmacodynamic
chorioangioma
apoplexy
laparotomy
glycosuria
cemetery
ectocytic
glycohemia
chorioid
hypothenar
dynamic
poikilocytosis
plethysmograph
oligomania
mononeuritis
oligocythemia
manigraphy
inosclerosis
hyperdynamia
monoma
colpitis

urolithic
monogenesis
plexalgia
dynamometer
bromatography
atelectasis
hormone
uronephrosis
hormonology
initis
inolith
inoma
alexia
hormonic
atelia
urologist
orthodiagraphy
basiphobia
ornithologist
euphony
cytogenesis

Notes:

LESSON III

32. List three additional English derivatives from each of the following Greek words:

    1. **mania**   2. **monos**   3. **glykys**

33. To what Greek word is each of the following related? Use the English word in a sentence to indicate its meaning:

    1. dynamic   2. initis   3. apoplexy

34. Indicate the meaning suggested by the endings of the following words:

1. epidemic	2. henotheism	3. metritis	4. narcotize
5. ostemia	6. kinetic	7. myxoid	8. prosthetist

35. Below the following group of six definitions are ten terms, only six of which are correct for the six definitions given. Place the number of each of the correct terms before the definition to which it belongs.

    ...... free from germs
    ...... a description of blood vessels and lymphatics
    ...... weakness
    ...... inflammation of a joint
    ...... exsection of a portion of the skull
    ...... excessive fear of disease

1. arthritis	2. craniotomy
3. aseptic	4. asthenia
5. angiography	6. craniectomy
7. nosophobia	8. thematic
9. septic	10. vessignon

36. Use a medical dictionary and provide a definition for each of the following words:

1. colpocystotomy	2. lordosis	3. monogenesis
4. chorioangioma	5. urolithic	6. rheometer
7. arthropod	8. asthenia	9. glycopenia

Notes:

LESSON IV

37. Vocabulary

pathos, n.: suffering, disease
trope, n.: a turning
leukos, adj.: white
blastos, n.: germ, sprout
krisis, -eos, n.: crisis
psora, n.: itch
derma, -atos, n.: skin
amphoteros, adj.: both
therme, n.: heat
meros, -eos, n.: part
kephale, n.: head
phlox, phlogos, n.: a flame

chroma, -atos, n.: color
kystis, -eos *and* -ios, n.: bladder
therapeia, n.: treatment
phero, v.: to bear, carry
kardia, n.: heart
klonos, n.: turmoil
glossa, n.: tongue
morphe, n.: form
helios, n.: sun
enkephalos, n.: brain
phlogistos, adj.: burnt, on fire
pyelos, n.: trough (pelvis)

38. Define etymologically:

cephalalgia
atelocardia
heliograph
leukoderma
cephalogenesis
mesocyst
heliosis
inotropic
psoric
dermatotherapy
leukocytopenia
clonic
meroacrania
bromatotherapy
leukocytotherapy
dermatosis
thermophobia
urocyst
thermodynamics
dermatoneurology
glossalgia
morphology
pathology
dermatotropic
chromophytosis
chromotherapy
morphogenesis

leukemia
chromatophobia
hormonotherapy
psoroid
isomeric
dermatomere
leukocytometer
mesencephalic
leukopenia
heliophobia
dermatosclerosis
dermatopathology
merocyte
leukocythemia
merotomy
leukocytoblast
cephalohemometer
athermic
pharmacotherapy
ateloglossia
dermatoid
glossology
glossotomy
metamorphosis
dermatopathophobia
glossodynamometer
morphic

mesoderm
cephalic
mesocytoma
pharmacomania
thermotropism
heliotherapy
dermatitis
ectodermic
merogenesis
mesoblastic
glycotropic
dermatography
cephalitis
urocystitis
endoderm
cephalometry
ectocardia
clonus
meronecrosis
thermotherapy
leukocytosis
oligomorphic
thermobiotic
dermatoma
glossitis
chromatopathy
perinephritis

Notes:

LESSON IV

39. Determine the meaning, pronunciation, and complete etymology of each of the following words:

1. leukomonocyte	2. amphoteric	3. isomerism
4. dermatotome	5. psoriasis	6. chromoblast
7. thermometer	8. chromatodermatosis	9. dermatalgia
10. poikiloderma	11. urocrisis	12. glossopathy
13. chromogenesis	14. mesencephalitis	15. mesoblast

40. Using vocabularies 20, 30, and 37 prepare a list of fifteen derivatives which would be of use to a pharmaceutical student. Consult a medical dictionary in order to determine the scientific and etymological meaning of each word on your list.

41. Match the columns by placing the correct numbers in the second column before each definition in the first column.

. . . . . . imperfect formation of the feet	1. ornithic
. . . . . . the study of food	2. inocyte
. . . . . . a fiber cell	3. bromatography
. . . . . . segmentation	4. dermatosis
. . . . . . an incision into the loin	5. cephalalgia
. . . . . . pertaining to birds	6. atelopodia
. . . . . . skin disease	7. inoma
. . . . . . headache	8. orthogamy
. . . . . . direct fertilization	9. laparotomy
. . . . . . a fiber tumor	10. merotomy

42. List prefixes or suffixes which may be used to indicate the following meanings:

1. negation	2. with	3. abnormal
4. place of	5. outside	6. belief
7. science of	8. good	9. around

Notes:

LESSON V

43. Vocabulary

phaios, adj.: dark, dusky
klysis, -eos, n.: injection
megas, megalou, adj.: great, large
omos, n.: shoulder
blennos, n.: mucus
pachys, adj.: thick
nystagmos, n.: nodding, dozing
odous, odontos, n.: tooth
tonos, n.: stretching, tension
ous, otos, n.: ear
larynx, laryngos, n.: larynx
phantasma, -atos, n.: image
iatreia, n.: medical treatment
kolon, n.: colon, large intestine
bathys, adj.: deep

kineo, v.: to move
kinesis, -eos, n.: motion, movement
akron, n.: point, extremity, summit
enteron, n.: intestine, bowel
opisthen, adv.: behind
rhis, rhinos, n.: nose
chole, n.: bile
moria, n.: folly
phyle, n.: tribe, class
odyne, n.: pain
aisthesis, -eos, n.: sensation, perception
oulon, n.: gum
bradys, adj.: slow

44. Define etymologically:

phantasmatology	laryngitis	paresthesia
otolith	odynometer	kinesimeter
hypodermoclysis	pachemia	megalomania
mesenteritis	acroneurosis	enterectomy
odontonosology	omalgia	otiatrics
megalakria	opisthotonos	rhinodynia
laryngotome	odynophobia	laryngotomy
amphotony	perienteritis	pachyderm
antinomy	pericholangitis	megalocardia
enteralgia	angiocholecystitis	odontodynia
enterotome	kinesalgia	acromegaly
acrophobia	megalocephalia	enteroclysis
otorhinolaryngology	phylogenesis	tonic
dysarteriotony	otoblennorrhea	rhinopathy
phantasmatomoria	pachyotia	mesentery
endocolitis	catatropia	kinesiology
megaloblast	megacephalic	epicrisis
acropathology	enterectasis	omitis
enterolith	kinesitherapy	rhinometer
phyletic	pachycephalia	odontopathy
otoneuralgia	rhinitis	hemicolectomy
dyslexia	uloglossitis	colpodynia
pyelonephrosis	bradylexia	esthesioblast
synesthesia	eukinesia	bathygastry

Notes:

LESSON V

45. Indicate the correct pronunciation of the following:

1. enteritis	2. otitis	3. tonicize
4. rhinorrhea	5. odontalgia	6. megaloglossia
7. otopathy	8. pericyte	9. kinesimeter

46. State the exact scientific definition of each of the following medical terms:

1. pheochromocytoma	2. tone	3. monomoria
4. erythroneocytosis	5. nosology	6. necrotomy
7. sepsometer	8. metronome	9. pyelotomy
10. megalocardia	11. odynophobia	12. glycohemia

47. Prepare a list of fifteen derivatives especially useful to a student of physiology. Indicate the etymological and scientific meaning of each word on your list.

48. Find as many English derivatives as you can from the following Greek words:

        1. **odous**   2. **rhis**

49. Transliterate the following Greek words into English:

1. βρῶμα	2. ἔρως	3. βουλή	4. ἀρχή
5. χολή	6. ταχύς	7. ἧπαρ	8. κακός
9. γάλα	10. δέρμα	11. φυλή	12. μανός
13. μέσος	14. μέγας	15. ἄκρον	16. δέρη

50. Supply the base of these Greek words:

1. cheir	2. dynamis	3. mania
4. phaios	5. pachys	6. larynx
7. thenar	8. rhis	9. chroma
10. ous	11. derma	12. megas
13. phlox	14. klysis	15. neos

Notes:

LESSON VI

51. Vocabulary

allos, adj.: other
sphygmos, n.: pulse
ops, opos, n.: eye, vision
opsis, -eos, and -ios, n.: vision
stoma, -atos, n.: mouth
melas, melanos, adj.: black
sphen, sphenos, n.: wedge
plastos, adj.: formed, molded
sitos, n.: food
pyknos, adj.: thick
splen, splenos, n.: spleen

manos, adj.: thin
arachne, n.: spider, cobweb
atmos, n.: vapor, steam
thesis, -eos, n.: placing, putting
amblys, adj.: dull
bole, n.: throw
ballo, v.: to throw
mnesis, -eos, n.: remembrance, memory
soma, -atos, n.: body
sphaira, n.: sphere, ball
dromos, n.: running

52. Define etymologically:

phlogistic	amblychromatic	stomatodynia
antiphlogistic	sitology	metabolism
allopathic	sphygmoid	paramnesia
atmometer	neoplastic	sitotherapy
somatotomy	sphenoid	otodynia
arachnoid	somatome	opsiometer
amnesia	neostomy	omarthritis
melanoma	arachnorhinitis	atmosphere
melancholia	pachyglossia	allocinesia
sphygmocardiograph	melanoderm	allogamy
analgic	anisometropia	somatology
prosthesis	pyknometer	sphenometer
acroscleroderma	anisoleukocytosis	odontitis
catabolism	amblyopia	enteric
sphygmomanometer	sitomania	stomatography
atmotherapy	pyknohemia	rhinalgia
melanoleukoderma	anabolic	colostomy
syndrome	heterodrome	alexia

53. Using a medical dictionary find the meaning and the complete etymology of ten of the following words:

1. nosomycosis
2. spondylopyosis
3. trophology
4. cardiomyoliposis
5. toponarcosis
6. zymophyte
7. stenostomia
8. olecranarthropathy
9. hypothyrosis
10. lymphocytopenia
11. gastrasthenia
12. ischemia
13. photodromy
14. cephalitis
15. heteronomy

Notes:

LESSON VI

54. Indicate the correct pronunciation of the first ten words in the second column of paragraph 52.

55. Find as many English derivatives as you are able from the following Greek words:

1. **sitos**   2. **stoma**   3. **atmos**

56. Match the columns by placing the correct numbers in the second column before each definition in the first column:

...... inflammation of the intestine	1. rhinodynia
...... inflammation of the tooth-pulp	2. otopathy
...... rhinalgia	3. stomatodynia
...... pain in the mouth	4. enteritis
...... diet therapy	5. odontitis
...... marbled skin	6. sitotherapy
...... an ear disease	7. melanoleukoderma
...... wedge-shaped	8. sphenoid
...... disease of the vagina	9. dermatoid
...... resembling skin	10. colpopathy

57. List two or more English derivatives from each of the following Greek words:

1. **opsios,** adj.: late
2. **myia,** n.: a fly
3. **kolla,** n.: glue

58. Transliterate the following Greek words into English:

1. κτείς   2. ταῖς   3. λίτος
4. μέτρον   5. γαστήρ   6. κρίσις

59. Using a medical dictionary provide the etymological and scientific meanings of each of the following medical terms:

1. gyromele   2. ithylordosis   3. meningomyelocele
4. odontonecrosis   5. urelcosis   6. synophrys
7. iatrogeny   8. hysterosalpingography   9. herpes

Notes:

LESSON VII

60. Vocabulary

tresis, -eos, n.: perforation, boring
dendron, n.: tree
syrinx, syringos, n.: tube, pipe
myxa, n.: mucus
stereos, adj.: solid
gametes, n.: spouse
gamete, n.: wife
telos, -eos, n.: completion, end
tele, adv.: far off
xanthos, adj.: yellow
oidema, -atos, n.: swelling
gnosis, -eos, n.: knowledge
lyo, v.: to loose
lysis, n.: loosening, dissolution

splanchnon, n.: viscus, entrail
brachys, adj.: short
mys, myos, n.: muscle
psyche, n.: mind
typos, n.: type
phago, v.: to eat
spondylos, n.: vertebra, spindle
myelos, n.: marrow
trophe, n.: nourishment
stigma, -atos, n.: point, mark
gnathos, n.: jaw
mikros, adj.: small
enantios, adj.: opposite, face to face

61. Define etymologically:

microgamy
dendrology
psychosomatic
psychic
diagnosis
nephredema
paralysis
xanthic
myopericarditis
trophoblast
myelo-encephalitis
hemolysis
microgenesis
teloblast
spondylotherapy
xanthopsia
psychoneurosis
gametocyte
esthesiogenic
isodynamic
dysphagia
cytogamy

spondylopathy
myosthenometer
stereometer
myelocyte
analysis
atresia
syringoid
myxasthenia
telephone
splanchnesthesia
myodynamometer
phagomania
syringomyelitis
splanchnodynia
myocardiograph
trophotherapy
stereognosis
gnathodynamometer
cardiolith
hypoleukemia
arthredema
paradiagnosis

teletherapy
trophocyte
splanchnic
dendroid
xanthochromia
brachygnathia
atelomyelia
psychology
stereotype
myxoma
pharmacognosy
prognosis
myokinesis
edema
telodendron
myelitis
microgamete
astigmatism
telekinesis
microbiophobia
dysbasia
exogamy

62. Show what changes the following Greek diphthongs undergo when coming into the English language:

1. αι   2. ει   3. οι   4. ου

Notes:

LESSON VII

63. Give the exact scientific meaning, pronunciation, and complete etymology of each word:

1. prosthetist	2. neopathy	3. melanoglossia
4. splanchnolith	5. myoendocarditis	6. myeloid
7. microlith	8. atresia	9. dermatology
10. thermology	11. trophic	12. microcolon
13. enantiomorphic	14. otorrhea	15. biogenesis

64. Prepare a list of fifteen Greek derivatives which would be useful to a student of anatomy. When the list is completed, determine the exact etymological and scientific meaning of each word.

65. List two or more derivatives from each of the following Greek words:

1. **arche, n.**: beginning, origin
2. **kyo, v.**: to conceive, be pregnant

66. Name the branch of medical science with which each of the following is concerned:

1. podology	2. neurology	3. angiology
4. nosology	5. pharmacology	6. dermatology
7. pathology	8. chiropody	9. glossology
10. craniology	11. otorhinolaryngology	12. somatology

67. Indicate when the accent of a Latin word is placed upon the penult.

68. Indicate when a syllable in a Latin word is considered long.

69. Supply the genitive ending and meaning of each of the following Greek words:

1. **derma**	2. **chroma**	3. **oidema**	4. **pous**
5. **is**	6. **ornis**	7. **odous**	8. **ous**

Notes:

LESSON VIII

REVIEW

70. Supply one meaning for each of the following prefixes and suffixes:

1. -oma	....	2. hyper-	....
3. ana-	....	4. -y	....
5. dia-	....	6. peri-	....
7. -osis	....	8. -ize	....
9. para-	....	10. hypo-	....
11. endo-	....	12. eu-	....
13. pro-	....	14. -oid	....

71. Transliterate the following Greek words into English:

1. νόμος	....	2. λόγος	....
3. μυελός	....	4. φιλέω	....
5. ταχύς	....	6. σῶμα	....
7. πόρος	....	8. μήτρα	....
9. πᾶς	....	10. φῦσα	....

72. Supply the base of the following Greek nouns:

1. tachos	....	2. thenar	....
3. ornis	....	4. genesis	....
5. odous	....	6. ous	....
7. atmos	....	8. akron	....
9. syrinx	....	10. phobia	....
11. cheir	....	12. splen	....
13. morphe	....	14. enkephalos	....

73. Provide the Greek word for each of the following terms:

1. jaw	....	2. hand	....
3. spleen	....	4. head	....
5. body	....	6. larynx	....
7. foot	....	8. skin	....
9. shoulder	....	10. vertebra	....
11. joint	....	12. muscle	....
13. skull	....	14. brain	....
15. kidney	....	16. nose	....
17. tongue	....	18. bladder	....

74. List three derivatives for each of the following Greek words:

1. bios	....	....	....
2. polys	....	....	....

REVIEW

3. **derma** ....
4. **rhis** ....
5. **homos** ....
6. **monos** ....
7. **kardia** ....
8. **soma** ....
9. **phobia** ....
10. **mikros** ....

75. Match the columns by placing the correct number in the second column before each Greek word in the first column:

...... **stigma**	1. shoulder
...... **ballo**	2. motion
...... **opsis**	3. white
...... **kinesis**	4. point
...... **leukos**	5. bent back
...... **basis**	6. to throw
...... **omos**	7. red
...... **helios**	8. step
...... **lordos**	9. sun
...... **erythros**	10. vision

76. Define etymologically:

1. neurohemal ....
....

2. rhinodynia ....
....

3. arthrectomy ....
....

4. laparoenterotomy ....
....

5. laryngopathy ....
....

6. isothermal ....
....

7. hypernephroid ....
....

8. periderm ....
....

9. hyponeocytosis ....
....

10. symbiosis ....
....

11. prognostic ....
....

REVIEW

12. spondylalgia ....

13. sympathy ....

14. splenitis ....

15. cololysis ....

16. megaloblast ....

17. neoplastic ....

18. pachycholia ....

19. metamorphosis ....

20. hemicardia ....

Notes:

LESSON IX

77. Vocabulary

lepsis, -eos, n.:   seizure
aktis, aktinos, n.:   ray
enchyma, -atos, n.:   infusion, juice
chondros, n.:   cartilage
kakos, n.:   bad
gaster (gastr-), gasteros, n.:   stomach
hexis, -eos, n.:   habit
hystera, n.:   uterus
koleos, n.:   sheath (vagina)
sapros, adj.:   putrid, rotten
thele, n.:   nipple
kopros, n.:   dung, feces
elektron, n.:   amber (rubbing of which causes electricity)

blepharon, n.:   eyelid
baros, n.:   weight, pressure
topos, n.:   place, region
thrombos, n.:   clot
koilia, n.:   belly
salpinx, salpingos, n.:   tube, trumpet
stenos, adj.:   narrow
stenosis, -eos, n.:   narrowing
klastos, adj.:   broken
phleps, phlebos, n.:   vein
chronos, n.:   time
osteon, n.:   bone
gramma, n.:   a drawing

78. Define etymologically:

celitis
phlebitis
isotope
thrombophlebitis
celiosalpingectomy
catalepsy
coleocystitis
polyuria
hysteromyotomy
osteotome
endothelioma
hysterolith
thromboangiitis
baragnosis
celiomyositis
bathycardia
encephalogram
microgastria

thrombosis
chronometer
parenchyma
stenostomia
gastrectasis
cachexia
barometer
coprophobia
blepharostenosis
coprophagy
salpingostomatomy
hysterodynia
gastro-enterocolitis
osteology
endosalpingitis
hysterotome
ulocace
periphlebitis

hysteritis
hypobaric
cacomorphosis
blepharitis
chondroclast
nomotopic
saprodontia
actinotherapy
saprophytic
salpingitis
cacotrophy
polyphagia
stenocephalia
chronology
hypernomic
paracolpitis
electrodynamometer
endosalpingitis

79. Give the meaning of the following words and one English word derived from each Greek word:

1. lithos
5. haima
2. isos
6. is
3. heteros
7. glykys
4. homos
8. ouron

Notes:

LESSON IX

80. Give the exact scientific meaning, and indicate the correct pronunciation of each word:

1. enantiobiosis
2. otitis
3. strobiloid
4. microlith
5. blepharotomy
6. copremia
7. gnathic
8. chondropathy
9. myoendocarditis
10. hysterology
11. dysosteogenesis
12. anabasis
13. anadenia
14. ergoesthesiograph
15. hysteropsychosis
16. iatrology

81. Below the following group of ten definitions are twelve terms, only ten of which are correct for the ten definitions given. Place the number of each of the correct terms before the definition to which it belongs:

...... the science of nutrition
...... earache
...... pain in the shoulder-joint
...... to produce tension in a part
...... inflammation of the nasal mucous membrane
...... incision of the uterus
...... a narrowing of the mouth
...... the classification of diseases
...... toothache
...... the evolutionary development of a plant

1. stenostomia
2. nosonomy
3. otiatrics
4. rhinitis
5. trophology
6. tonicize
7. ornithic
8. hysterotomy
9. phylogenesis
10. otalgia
11. omalgia
12. odontodynia

82. List the prefixes which may be used to indicate the following meanings:

1. excessive
2. upon
3. lack of
4. within
5. against
6. without
7. around
8. beside
9. together

Notes:

LESSON X

83. Vocabulary

skopeo, v.: to look at, view
presbys, adj.: old, pertaining to old age
trypesis, -eos, n.: piercing
narke, n.: stupor
hydor (hydr-), hydatos, n.: water
pneuma, -atos, n.: air, wind, breath
pneumon, n.: lung
phileo, v.: to love
lipos, n.: fat
gyne, gynaikos, n.: woman
anthropos, n.: man
schizo, v.: to split, divide

pas, pantos, adj.: all, complete
ergon, n.: work, energy
phren, phrenos, n.: mind
nyx, nyktos, n.: night
stethos, n.: breast
techne, n.: skill
theion, n.: sulphur
thorax, thorakos, n.: chest
thrix, trichos, n.: hair
osmos, n.: impulsion
sarx, sarkos, n.: flesh
skotos, n.: darkness

84. Define etymologically:

lipocyte
osmosis
scototherapy
enterocystoma
dysgalactia
pneumolith
celioma
philanthropy
stethoscope
nyctophobia
pericyte
pantomorphic
lipocardiac
salpingotomy
narcomania
gynaecology
sphygmodynamometer
osteophony
hysterostomatomy

pneumonia
narcolysis
sarcoma
rhinolaryngitis
hemiglossectomy
splanchnomegalia
schizotrichia
allergy
hydrosphygmograph
stethomyitis
hydropneumothorax
stomatopathy
allokinetic
pantophobia
technic
hydrothionuria
myocyte
pneumohemothorax
enteritis

pneumatocardia
craniotrypesis
hydrometer
pansclerosis
phlogocyte
phagotherapy
chondrology
ergophobia
schizophrenia
narcolepsy
endothermic
presbyophrenia
gastrocolitis
odontic
pneumaturia
microcardia
gnathodynia
lipophilic
rhinorrhea

85. List three or more English words derived from each of the following Greek words:

1. **ankyra, n.**: anchor, hook
2. **zyme, n.**: leaven
3. **akouo, v.**: to hear
4. **asthma, n.**: hard-drawn breath

Notes:

LESSON X

86. Determine the meaning, pronunciation, and complete etymology of each word:

1. odontorthosis
2. chondrogenesis
3. enterology
4. gastrasthenia
5. myoid
6. celiomyositis
7. ostemia
8. thrombogenesis
9. barometrograph
10. microbiology

87. Prepare a list of twenty derivatives especially useful to an anthropologist. When the list is completed, consult an unabridged dictionary and show both the etymological and scientific meaning of each word on your list.

88. Write the number of the correct matching word in the second column before its definition in the first column.

...... inflammation of both bone and cartilage
...... neuralgic pain in the ear
...... pain in the bone
...... any uterine disease
...... the development of bone
...... disease of the viscera
...... a disease of the ear
...... a debilitated state of the ear muscles
...... like a cobweb
...... medical

1. hysteropathy
2. otopathy
3. osteogenesis
4. osteodynia
5. otomyasthenia
6. osteochondritis
7. otoneuralgia
8. splanchnopathy
9. iatric
10. arachnoid

89. Indicate the base of these Greek words:

1. kopros
2. phelps
3. arche
4. stigma
5. gnathos
6. gametes
7. syrinx
8. melas
9. soma

90. Supply a Greek word for each of the following terms:

1. eyelid
2. bone
3. belly
4. finger
5. arm
6. heart
7. lung
8. nerve
9. lip
10. chest
11. tooth
12. stomach

Notes:

LESSON XI

91. Vocabulary

hen, henos, num.: one
daktylos, n.: finger
theos, n.: God
hekaton, num.: hundred
parthenos, n.: maiden
trauma, -atos, n.: wound
hepta, num.: seven
thalassa, n.: sea
pente, num.: five
phos, photos, n.: light
demos, n.: people
ichthys, ichthyos, n.: fish
pharynx, pharyngos, n.: throat

hymen, hymenos, n.: membrane
tetra, tetrados, num.: four
hepar, hepatos, n.: liver
aner, andros, n.: man, male
thanatos, n.: death
geron, gerontos, n.: old man
phallos, n.: penis
helmin, helminthos, n.: worm
hex, num.: six
cheilos, n.: lip
pithekos, n.: ape
orchis, -ios and -eos, n.: testicle
pepsis, -eos, n.: digestion

92. Define etymologically:

otologist
rhinotomy
henotheism
thanatobiologic
gerontology
thalassotherapy
traumatic
ichthyophagy
dysentery
photopharmacology
spondylodynia
androphobia
amphidiarthrosis
tetrachromic
thanatoid
helminthophobia
epidemic
dyspepsia

dactylomegaly
chilotomy
epicyte
microcolon
myelotome
hydronephrosis
henogenesis
theology
hepatalgia
pentadactyl
phallitis
pithecoid
hectometer
hepatitis
ectoblast
gastralgia
orchic
parahepatitis

tetrablastic
helminthoid
ecsomatics
pharyngolith
sapremia
parthenogenesis
enteromegalia
hymenotome
xanthoderm
myopathy
lipoma
dactylitis
hymenology
cheilophagia
pandemic
chondrocyte
schizophrenic
electrocardiogram

93. Give the meaning of the following words and one English word derived from each Greek word:

1. cheir   2. orthos   3. pous   4. arthron   5. nomos
6. gala   7. nekros   8. monos   9. therme   10. kardia

Notes:

LESSON XI

94. Give the exact scientific definition and indicate the correct pronunciation of each of the following:

1. gastritis
2. hepatodynia
3. pneumonemia
4. helminthoma
5. lipophagic
6. thanatology
7. narcotize
8. ichthyology
9. panhysterectomy
10. orchialgia

95. Name the form, shape, or likeness indicated by each of the following words:

1. geoid
2. chorioid
3. myxoid
4. dermatoid
5. odontoid
6. neuroid
7. dendroid
8. myeloid
9. syringoid
10. angioid
11. encephaloid
12. splenoid
13. gynecoid
14. myoid
15. android

96. Match the columns by placing the correct numbers in the second column before each definition in the first column:

```
......  the treatment of wounds and injuries        1.  hymenotome
......  sensitiveness to light                      2.  traumatotherapy
......  biting of the lips                          3.  hepatotomy
......  malformation                                4.  dysmorphosis
......  an instrument for cutting membranes         5.  pithecoid
......  incision into the liver                     6.  photesthesis
......  fusion of the testicles                     7.  synorchism
......  a treatise on death                         8.  cheilophagia
......  a tumor which surrounds a blood vessel      9.  periangioma
......  apelike                                    10.  thanatography
```

97. Supply a Greek word for each of the following terms:

1. vessel
2. perforation
3. artery
4. disease
5. blood
6. impulsion
7. injection
8. stretching
9. swelling
10. treatment
11. vein
12. mucus

Notes:

LESSON XII

98. Vocabulary

pais, paidos, n.: child
hygros, adj.: moist
ichor, ichoros, n.: serum, discharge
sporos, n.: seed
kreas, kreos, n.: flesh
hidros, n.: sweat
hyalos, n.: glass
gymnos, adj.: naked
nepios, n.: infant
omphalos, n.: navel
onkos, n.: tumor
osme, n.: smell
makros, adj.: large, long

delos, adj.: evident, clear
lepis, lepidos, n.: scale
labros, adj.: greedy
echo, echoos, n.: echo
eros, erotos, n.: love
aden, adenos, n.: gland
proktos, n.: anus, rectum
leios, adj.: smooth
elaion, n.: oil
sperma, -atos, n.: seed
metra, n.: womb, uterus
histos, n.: tissue
phoresis, -eos, n.: a carrying in

99. Define etymologically:

omphalitis
proctectasia
enhematospore
erotology
enterotropic
histography
macrotia
sphygmophone
splanchnosomatic
xanthoma
cacosmia
melanuria
omphalophlebitis
echophony
delomorphic
creophagism
perimetritis
electrophoresis

hygroma
elaiometer
labrocyte
gymnosperm
peridontia
lepidic
nystagmic
amnesiac
endometrectomy
gynopathic
microcardia
gymnospore
epidermatoplasty
macrospore
oncology
leiomyoma
myodynia
anaphoresis

ichoroid
leioderma
endometritis
kinetic
rhinolith
gymnocyte
paidology
stomatologist
proctotome
myxoid
psychopathy
anhidrosis
hyalophagia
adenodynia
nepiology
hidradenitis
myeloma
paradenditis

100. Supply the genitive ending and the meaning of each of the following Greek words:

1. gaster
2. geron
3. phos
4. hepar
5. aner
6. stigma
7. syrinx
9. gyne
9. thrix
10. thorax
11. nyx
12. ornis

Notes:

LESSON XII

101. List two or more English words derived from each of the following Greek words:

     1. **kele,** n.:   tumor, rupture
     2. **zoon,** n.:   animal
     3. **sphyzo,** v.:   to beat, throb
     4. **xenos,** n.:   stranger, foreigner, guest

102. Match the following phobias with their definitions:

Phobia	*Fear of*
...... monophobia	1. high places
...... heliophobia	2. places
...... nosophobia	3. drugs
...... panphobia	4. food
...... gamophobia	5. marriage
...... pediophobia	6. the sun
...... chromatophobia	7. being alone
...... necrophobia	8. light
...... dysmorphophobia	9. children
...... photophobia	10. corpses
...... topophobia	11. colors
...... odynephobia	12. deformity
...... sitophobia	13. pain
...... pharmacophobia	14. everything
...... acrophobia	15. disease

103. Match the following Greek words with their English equivalents:

...... thanatos	1. ray
...... osmos	2. nourishment
...... aktis	3. black
...... lepsis	4. itch
...... trophe	5. death
...... melas	6. bile
...... chole	7. color
...... phyle	8. impulsion
...... chroma	9. class
...... psora	10. seizure

Notes:

LESSON XIII

104. Vocabulary

boutyron, n.: butter
miseo, v.: to hate
boule, n.: will
palaios, adj.: old, ancient
piesis, -eos, n.: pressure
bronchos, n.: windpipe
dis, adv.: twice, double
ixys, ixyos, n.: waist
oxys, adj.: sharp, sour
didymos, n.: twin (testicles)
plane, n.: wandering
aer, aeros, n.: air
bous, n.: ox

tyros, n.: cheese
kainos, adj.: new
delphys, delphyos, n.: uterus
skelos, n.: leg
kyon, kynikos, n.: dog
karkinoma, -atos, n.: cancer
emesis, -eos, n.: vomiting
laleo, v.: to speak
konis, konios, n.: dust
mechane, n.: machine
skor, skatos, n.: feces, dung
brachion, n.: arm
limos, n.: hunger

105. Define etymologically:

piesimeter
stigmatic
butyric
dimorphic
coniology
ixomyelitis
hydrophobia
euthanasia
erotic
alalia
osteoid
didymalgia
brachialgia
eutrophic
odontoma
hydrocystoma
metratome
misogamy
bulimia

emetic
misanthropia
chronobiology
palaeolithic
bronchadenitis
narcotic
hepatocolic
oxyosmia
didymitis
misocainia
hyperbulia
scatology
proctocolitis
hygrometer
chromocyte
tonicize
trichoid
omphalectomy
limosis

abulia
carcinomatosis
trichophobia
scelalgia
histology
technologist
didelphic
uroplania
omphaloma
tyroid
orchitis
mechanotherapy
cynocephalic
aerendocardia
thermograph
microcyte
cheilitis
histic
arthroscope

106. Supply two or more English words derived from each of the following Greek words:

1. zoe, n.: life
2. kauter, kauteros, n.: branding iron

Notes:

LESSON XIII

107. Give the scientific meaning and the complete etymology of each of the following medical terms:

1. carcinomatophobia	2. oncotomy	3. butyroid
4. metritis	5. tyroma	6. cheilotomy
7. didymodynia	8. pneumonopathy	9. macrostomia
10. metralgia	11. hyalophobia	12. sporogenesis
13. histogenesis	14. hepatectomy	15. trichology
16. thalassophobia	17. hydrotherapy	18. traumatotherapy
19. panarthritis	20. cheilectomy	21. narcosis
22. hepatonephritis	23. chondroid	24. pneumonectasia

108. Prepare a list of twenty-five derivatives which would be useful to a student of anatomy. Consult a medical dictionary in order to determine the scientific and etymological meaning of each word on your list.

109. Match the columns by placing the correct numbers in the second column before each definition in the first column:

...... the study of tumors	1. lipocardiac
...... disease of a testicle	2. orchiopathy
...... pertaining to a fatty heart	3. myeloid
...... relating to bone marrow	4. panhidrosis
...... universal sweating	5. hyalophagia
...... inflammation of the uterus	6. lipoma
...... insane eating of glass	7. oncology
...... a tumor of fatty tissue	8. metritis
...... hardening of the joints	9. hypatodynia
...... pain in the liver	10. arthrosclerosis
...... incision of the uterus	11. hysterotomy
...... pain in the chest	12. cystodynia
...... poor memory	13. synchronous
...... canine tooth	14. otitis
...... incision of the liver	15. atmotherapy
...... inflammation of the ear	16. cynodont
...... pain in the bladder	17. dysmnesia
...... happening at the same time	18. theotherapy
...... formation of bony tissue	19. thoracodynia
...... treatment by medical vapors	20. osteosis
...... treatment by means of religious exercises	21. hepatotomy

Notes:

LESSON XIV

110. Vocabulary

polis, -eos *and* -ios, n.: city
deuteros, adj.: second
trochos, n.: wheel
pyon, n.: pus
desmos, n.: ligament, fetter
melos, n.: limb
potamos, n.: river
eos, n.: dawn
hippos, n.: horse
ōon, n.: egg
peros, adj.: maimed

helix, -ikos, n.: coil
argyros, n.: silver
hals, halos, n.: salt
oros, n.: whey
pepto, v.: to digest
orrhos, n.: serum
skaphe, n.: boat
onyma, -atos, n.: name
dere, n.: neck
ktesis, ktenos, n.: comb
bapto, v.: to dip, dye

111. Define etymologically:

helicopodia
pyoid
megaloglossia
myocardiac
histoma
pseudomnesia
hippopotamus
oosperm
laryngorhinology
hymenitis
hydrokinetics
trochoid
eolith
baptize
neoblastic
gymnophobia
lalophobia
macropodia
cheilitis

hypomegasoma
deuteronomy
otopathy
elaioma
deradenitis
proctodynia
orotherapy
prognosis
antipyogenic
phagocyte
omphalic
haloid
allogamy
pyohemothorax
peropus
osteoma
histoid
carcinomatoid
proctitis

necropolis
peptic
scaphocephalic
colonitis
hygrostomia
monobulia
trichophagy
orrhology
desmectasia
halophyte
ctenoid
exogenesis
potamophobia
ergometer
litharge
synonym
desmotomy
abulomania
omphalogenesis

112. Give the scientific definition and the complete etymology of each of the following words:

1. oosome
4. pyodermatitis
7. desmoid

2. sporocyst
5. pantalgia
8. pyocyte

3. carcinoma
6. pneumonotomy
9. microglossia

Notes:

LESSON XIV

113. Below the following groups of eight definitions are nine terms, only eight of which are correct for the eight definitions given. Place the number of each of the correct terms before the definition to which it belongs:

Group I

...... a description of disease   ...... the division of a ligament
...... abnormal slowness in eating   ...... veterinary medicine
...... silver poisoning   ...... abnormal slowness in movement
...... the measurement of a solid   ...... a description of the ligaments
     object

1. argyrosis	2. hippiatrics	3. pathography
4. desmography	5. bradyphagia	6. stereometry
7. desmotomy	8. bradycinesia	9. endometrectomy

Group II

...... a pus-tube   ...... slowness of digestion
...... the formation of pus   ...... the digestive tract
...... round-headedness   ...... a constant discharge of pus
...... pertaining to the liver and   ...... abnormal slowness in reading
     lungs

1. pyosalpinx	2. pyorrhea	3. peptogaster
4. bradylexia	5. hypatodynia	6. pyogenesis
7. bradypepsia	8. trochocephalia	9. hepatopneumonic

114. Supply the medical definition of each of the following words:

1. leukocyte	2. narcomaniac	3. glossectomy
4. tricholith	5. hepatic	6. phallagia
7. thanatophobia	8. hygric	9. elaiopathy
10. proctology	11. anaphia	12. orchic

115. Supply two or more English words derived from each of the following Greek words:

1. **allotrios,** adj.: foreign, strange
2. **karpos,** n.: wrist
3. **helkos,** n.: ulcer
4. **hebe,** n.: youth
5. **kylindros,** n.: roll

Notes:

LESSON XV

116. Vocabulary

archos n.: rectum	**treis, tria,** num.: three
pyle, n.: gate	**stear, steatos,** n.: tallow, fat
ptosis, -eos, n.: falling	**rhachis (rach-), -ios,** n.: spine
orexis, -eos, n.: appetite	**therion,** n.: wild beast
porne, n.: prostitute	**bakterion,** n.: rod, staff
mastos, n.: breast	**hapto,** v.: to touch
ankyle, n.: stiff joint	**kyanos,** n.: dark blue substance
klon, n.: twig, shoot	**prosopon,** n.: face
seismos, n.: shaking, shock	**typhlos,** adj.: blind
holos, adj.: whole, entire	**kryos,** adj.: cold
chorde, n.: cord	**phoros,** adj.: bearing
amylon, n.: starch	**theka,** n.: box, case
thymos, n.: spirit, mind	**chloros,** adj.: green
autos, pron.: self	**trigonon,** n.: triangle
tricha, adj.: threefold	**ektrosis, -eos,** n.: miscarriage

117. Define etymologically:

monoclonal	rachiopathy	clonogenic
haptics	archoptosia	autogenesis
gastrocele	chloroblast	archocystocoloposyrinx
mastodynia	trachelodynia	opthalmomyiasis
cyanuria	microbrachia	hydropyonephrosis
trigonocephalic	cyrobiology	ankyloblepharon
pornography	ectrogenic	holoanencephaly
telekinesis	bacterialysis	prosoponeuralgia
hologynic	cyanopsia	hypothymergasis
amyloclast	thecoma	ankylodactylia
typhlosis	xanthoderma	pheochromocyte
colpocystitis	theriomorphism	heterotrichosis
electrophore	perimastitis	steatocystoma
dysthymia	pyelophlebitis	autophagia
haptometer	pylephlebectasia	zymogenic
ulocarcinoma	archostenosis	antimicrobics
spodogram	dysorexia	bacteriophage
trigastric	amylemia	thymokinetic
alexia	epichordal	endotheliosis
cyropathy	autonomy	mesometritis
seismesthesia	hypomastia	trichromatopsia
chordoma	theriatrics	craniophore
anorexia	tomography	ectrodactyl

118. Indicate the fear associated with each of the following words:

1. phagophobia	2. gynephobia	3. autophobia
4. androphobia	5. nyctophobia	6. hypnophobia
7. thermophobia	8. dermatophobia	9. phobophobia

Notes:

LESSON XV

119. Match the following Greek words and their English equivalents:

...... bathys	1. digestion
...... elektron	2. part
...... pepsis	3. bosom
..... phoresis	4. flesh
...... bradys	5. hear
...... meros	6. a carrying in
...... kolpos	7. ulcer
...... helkos	8. deep
...... akouo	9. amber
...... sarx	10. slow

120. Supply the medical definition of each of the following words:

1. thromboendocarditis	2. heteronomy	3. endorphin
4. antimicrobics	5. monochromatic	6. isoelectric
7. anaerobic	8. polyodontia	9. stethomyitis

121. Identify the following parts of the body:

1. daktylos	2. oulon	3. pneumon
4. phallos	5. kephale	6. mastos
7. archos	8. brachion	9. prosopon
10. thele	11. ixys	12. gaster

122. Prepare a list of fifteen derivatives which would be useful to a student of psychiatry. Consult a medical dictionary in order to determine the scientific and etymological meaning of each word on your list.

123. Below the following group of six definitions are ten terms, only six of which are correct for the six definitions given. Place the number of each of the correct terms before the definition to which it belongs.

...... inflammation of the colon	1. prostatitis
...... inflammation of a vocal cord	2. cystitis
...... inflammation of a cartilage	3. arthritis
•..... inflammation of the liver	4. colitis
...... inflammation of the bladder	5. hepatitis
...... inflammation of the periosteum	6. chronditis
	7. myelitis
	8. periostitis
	9. splenitis
	10. chorditis

Notes:

Medical Greek and Latin Workbook

Notes:

LESSON XVI

GENERAL REVIEW

124. Supply the meanings of the following Greek words:

1. pais	....	2. elaion	....
3. konis	....	4. ornis	....
5. meros	....	6. megas	....
7. sitos	....	8. mys	....
9. hystera	....	10. theos	....
11. phren	....	12. hippos	....
13. thrix	....	14. gnathos	....
15. bronchos.	....	16. chole	....

125. Indicate the meaning of each of the following prefixes and suffixes:

1. pro-	....	2. par-	....
3. -itis	....	4. endo-	....
5. dys-	....	6. -etic	....
7. ap-	....	8. eu-	....
9. anti-	....	10. -osis	....
11. -oid	....	12. meth-	....
13. -ize	....	14. -tery	....
15. -gen	....	16. a-	....

126. Supply the genitive ending and the meaning of each of the following Greek words:

1. kyon ....
2. geron ....
3. ichor ....
4. thorax ....
5. pous ....
6. rhis ....
7. is ....
8. ous ....
9. chroma ....
10. gala ....

127. Translate the following Greek words into English .

1. ὕαλος ....
2. μέλος ....
3. γαστήρ ....
4. δέρμα ....
5. ἄλγος ....
6. πάθος ....

GENERAL REVIEW

7. χόνδρος   ....
8. βλέφαρον   ....
9. αἴσθησις   ....
10. θάνατος   ....

128. List three derivatives for each of the following Greek words:

1. nephros ....
2. neos   ....
3. haima   ....
4. lapara   ....
5. derma   ....
6. rhis   ....
7. syrinx   ....
8. koleos   ....
9. lipos   ....
10. thanatos ....

129. Define etymologically:

1. erythroneocytosis ....

2. omphalogenesis ....

3. panhysterectomy ....

4. chondrocyte ....

5. xanthoderm ....

6. melanoglossia ....

7. rhinolith ....

8. chromatophobia ....

9. mesoneuritis ....

10. ichthyology ....

11. anthroposomatology ....

12. hysterosalpingostomy ....

13. sphygmodynamometer...
....

GENERAL REVIEW

14. rhinolaryngitis ....
15. osteoarthropathy ....
16. chromatelopsia ....
17. bradypepsia ....
18. orchiencephaloma ....
19. bradylexia ....
20. electrocardiophonography ....

130. Name the form, shape, or likeness indicated by each of the following words:

1. arachnoid	2. anthropoid ....
3. pithecoid	4. hyaloid ....
5. butyroid	6. lipoid ....
7. sarcoid	8. histoid ....
9. adenoid	10. phleboid ....
11. odontoid	12. dermoid ....
13. scleroid	14. histoid ....
15. dendroid	16. thanatoid ....

131. Name the part of the body that would be affected by the following pains:

1. chiralgia	2. cephalalgia ....
3. glossalgia	4. rhinodynia ....
5. odontodynia	6. hepatodynia ....
7. orchialgia	8. spondylodynia ....
9. otodynia	10. neuralgia ....
11. enteralgia	12. omalgia ....
13. gnathodynia	14. gastralgia ....
15. hysterodynia	16. podalgia ....

132. Name the part of the body into which each of the following incisions is made:

1. blepharotomy ....
2. splenotomy ....
3. nephrotomy...
4. ototomy ....
5. rhinotomy ....

GENERAL REVIEW

6. laryngotomy ....
7. celiotomy ....
8. salpingotomy...
9. arteriotomy ....
10. omphalectomy ....
11. pyelotomy ....
12. hemicolectomy ....
13. carpectomy ....
14. hysterotomy ....
15. orchiotomy ....

133. Name the branch of medical science with which each of the following is concerned:

1. gastroenterology ....   2. hematology ....
3. odontology   ....   4. gynecology ....
5. gerontology   ....   6. nephrology ....
7. phlebology   ....   8. thanatology ....
9. opthalmology   ....   10. osteology   ....

134. Identify the following parts of the body:

1. derma ....   2. omos   ....
3. enteron ....   4. hepar   ....
5. stethos ....   6. rhis   ....
7. kardia ....   8. nephros   ....
9. odous ....   10. dere   ....
11. metra ....   12. ous   ....
13. gnathos ....   14. blepharon ....
15. proktos ....   16. koleos   ....
17. hystera ....   18. gnathos   ....

135. Below the following groups of eight definitions are ten terms, only eight of which are correct for the eight definitions given. Place the number of each of the correct terms before the definition to which it belongs.

Group I

..... abnormally large size of the body
..... hatred of women
..... expansion of the colon with gas
..... the curdling of milk
..... expansion of the rectum
..... an acute disease
..... expansion of the intestine with gas
..... fear of dogs

1. aerophyte   2. tyrosis   3. cynophobia   4. oxypathia
5. macrosomia   6. emetic   7. aerocoly   8. misogyny
9. proctectasia   10. aerenterectasia

GENERAL REVIEW

Group II

..... production of cancer
..... an air plant
..... swallowing of air
..... study of disease in prehistoric
     times

..... a disease caused by dust
..... inflammation of a testicle
..... pertaining to vomiting
..... any disease of the ligaments

1. macrosomia   2. desmopathy   3. emetic   4. aerophyte
5. aerogastria   6. coniosis   7. aerophagia   8. didymitis
9. paleopathology   10. carcinogenesis

Group III

..... inflammation of a joint
..... the science of vocal sounds
..... star-shaped
..... inflammation of the urinary
     bladder

..... a white blood corpuscle
..... a disease of the tongue
..... the science of heat
..... congenital absence of the feet

1. glossopathy   2. astroid   3. apodia   4. leukocyte
5. thermology   6. leukemia   7. arthritis   8. phonology
9. dermatitis   10. urocystitis

Group IV

..... pertaining to the viscera and
     body
..... pertaining to the pulse
..... organically ill
..... inflammation of the fallopian
     tube

..... enlargement of the spleen
..... dietetics
..... constricted
..... pertaining to an examination
     of the chest

1. salpingitis   2. stasimorphia   3. sphygmic   4. somatopathic
5. splanchnosomatic   6. splenelcosis   7. stethoscopic   8. sitology
9. stenotic   10. splenectasia

Part Two

MEDICAL LATIN

Medical Latin

1. The Latin Alphabet

The Latin alphabet is the same as the English except that it has no *w*. *U* supplies the place of *w:* sang*u*is.

2. The Roman Method of Pronunciation

(a) The vowels *a*, *e*, *i*, *o*, *u* and *y* are pronounced as follows:

Long Vowels	*Short Vowels*
a as in *father*	**a** as in *idea*
e as in *they*	**e** as in *met*
i as in *machine*	**i** as in *pit*
o as in *holy*	**o** as in *obey*
u as in *rule*	**u** as in *full*
y as French *u*	

(b) Diphthongs are pronounced thus:

ae like *ay*	**au** like *ow* in *how*
ei as in *eight*	**eu** as *ehoo*
ui as *we*	**oe** like *oy*

(c) The consonants are pronounced as they are in English except for the following letters:

c and **g** are always hard, as in *come* and *get*
s as in *sea*
j as *y* in *yet*
v like *w* in *wine*

Note: In medical Latin some people prefer to use the English method of pronunciation. In this method all vowels, diphthongs, and consonants have the same sounds as in English.

3. Syllabification

(a) A word has as many syllables as it has vowels and diphthongs.

(b) A single consonant between two vowels is taken with the vowel that follows: **fe-ro, fo-ra-men.**

(c) When there are two or more consonants between vowels all but the first are joined with the following vowel: **fos-sa, fe-nes-tra.** However, a consonant followed by *l* or *r* is generally taken with the vowel that follows: **fi-bra.**

(d) In compounds, the prepositional element is ordinarily separated: **ad-est.**

4. Accentuation and Quantity

(a) Words of two syllables are always accented on the first syllable: **áqua.** Words of more than two syllables are accented on the penult, if it is long: **sagítta;** if the penult is short, the antepenult is accented: **óculus.**

(b) A syllable is long if it contains a long vowel or diphthong, or if the vowel is followed by two consonants or by a double consonant (*x, z*).

COMBINING TECHNIQUES

5. Latin Nouns

Latin nouns are inflected in five declensions. The connective vowel **i,** less frequently **o** or **u,** is generally added to the base of the Latin noun to make a combining form for compound words. The base may be found by dropping the case-ending of the genitive singular.

(a) **First or A-Declension nouns** have **-ae** as the case-ending in the genitive singular:

Nom.	*Gen.*	*Meaning*	*Base*	*Comb. form*	*Example*
aqua	aquae	water	aqu	aqui-	aquiferous
musca	muscae	fly	musc	musci-	muscicide
costa	costae	rib	cost	costo-	costoscapular

Note: Silent **e** is often added to the base to form English words: **rosa, rosae,** *rose.* Silent **e** is here added to the base (**ros**) to form the English word *rose.*

(b) **Second or O-Declension nouns** have **-i** as the case-ending in the genitive singular:

Nom.	Gen.	Meaning	Base	Comb. form	Example
ramus	rami	branch	ram	rami-	ramiform
puer	pueri	boy	puer	pueri-	puericulture
vir	viri	man	vir	viri-	viripotent
vitrum	vitri	glass	vitr	vitri-	vitrify

(c) **Third or Consonant or I-Declension nouns,** while having various forms in the nominative singular, always form the genitive singular in -is:

Nom.	Gen.	Meaning	Base	Comb. form	Example
pes	pedis	foot	ped	pedi-	pedicure
lens	lentis	lens	lent	lenti-	lenticonus
homo	hominis	man	homin	homini-	homininoxious
venter	ventris	belly	ventr	ventri-	ventriduct
cutis	cutis	skin	cut	cuti-	cutireaction
radix	radicis	root	radic	radici-	radiciform

(d) **Fourth or U-Declension nouns** have -us as the case-ending in the genitive singular. The combining form is either i or u:

Nom.	Gen.	Meaning	Base	Comb. form	Example
fructus	fructus	fruit	fruct	fructi-	fructiferous
cornu	cornus	horn	corn	cornu-	cornucopia

(e) **Fifth or E-Declension nouns** have -ei as the case-ending in the genitive singular:

Nom.	Gen.	Meaning	Base	Comb. form	Example
species	speciei	form	speci	speci-	specify
facies	faciei	face	faci	faci-	facial

6. Latin Adjectives

The adjective is that part of speech which is used to qualify nouns: **bonus,** good. An adjective must agree with the noun which it qualifies in number, gender, and case: **ramus bonus,** a good branch; **regula bona,** a good rule; **signum bonum,** a good sign. In general, adjectives are formed and declined like nouns. Some adjectives are partly of the first and second declensions while the rest are of the third. (See Paragraph 8 for inflections of adjectives.) To make the combining form, add the connective vowel i to the adjectival base.

7. Latin Verbs

Latin verbs have a present active indicative ending in **-o** or **-or**: **gusto, miror**. The verbal base is found by dropping these endings: **gust, mir**. Prefixes and suffixes may be added to the verbal base to form English words:

Verb	Meaning	Base	Example
gusto	taste	gust	disgust
flecto	bend	flect	inflection
misceo	mix	misce	miscegenation
audio	hear	audi	inaudible
miror	wonder	mir	admirable

The past participles of Latin verbs end in **-us**: **gustatus**. The participial base is found by dropping the final **-us**: **gustat**. Prefixes and suffixes may be added to the verbal base to form English words:

Past Participle	Meaning	Base	Example
gustatus	tasted	gustat	gustatory
flexus	bent	flex	flexibility
mixtus	mixed	mixt	mixture
auditus	heard	audit	audition

Note: Silent **e** is often added to verbal and participial bases to form English words: **maturo, maturatus**, *to ripen*. Silent **e** is here added to the verbal bases (**matur, maturat**) to form the English words *mature* and *maturate*.

8. Tables of Declensions

Case Endings of the Five Declensions

	1	2		3		4		5
	F.	M.	N.	M.F.	N.	M.	N.	F.
Sing.								
Nom.	-a	-us, -er	-um	(Various)	(Various)	-us	-u	-es
Gen.	-ae	-i	-i	-is	-is	-us	-us	-ei
Plur.								
Nom.	-ae	-i	-a	-es	-a, -ia	-us	-ua	-es
Gen.	-arum	-orum	-orum	-um, -ium	-um, -ium	-uum	-uum	-erum

Adjectives

Adjectives of the First and Second Declension:

Singular	Masculine	Feminine	Neuter	Meaning
Nominative	purus	pura	purum	pure
Genitive	puri	purae	puri	
Plural				
Nominative	puri	purae	pura	
Genitive	purorum	purarum	purorum	

Singular	Masculine	Feminine	Neuter	
Nominative	liber	libera	liberum	free
Genitive	liberi	liberae	liberi	
Plural				
Nominative	liberi	liberae	libera	
Genitive	liberorum	liberarum	liberorum	

Singular	Masculine	Feminine	Neuter	
Nominative	pulcher	pulchra	pulchrum	beautiful
Genitive	pulchri	pulchrae	pulchri	
Plural				
Nominative	pulchri	pulchrae	pulchra	
Genitive	pulchrorum	pulchrarum	pulchrorum	

Third Declension Adjectives—Adjectives of Three Terminations:

Singular	Masculine	Feminine	Neuter	
Nominative	acer	acris	acre	sharp
Genitive	acris	acris	acris	
Plural				
Nominative	acres	acres	acria	
Genitive	acrium	acrium	acrium	

Third Declension Adjectives—Adjectives of Two Terminations:

Singular	Masculine or Feminine	Neuter	
Nominative	fortis	forte	strong
Genitive	fortis	fortis	
Plural			
Nominative	fortes	fortia	
Genitive	fortium	fortium	

Third Declension Adjectives—Adjectives of One Termination:

Singular	Masculine or Feminine	Neuter	
Nominative	potens	potens	powerful
Genitive	potentis	potentis	
Plural			
Nominative	potentes	potentia	
Genitive	potentium	potentium	

Third Declension Adjectives—Comparative Adjectives:

Singular	Masculine or Feminine	Neuter	
Nominative	inferior	inferius	lower
Genitive	inferioris	inferioris	
Plural			
Nominative	inferiores	inferiora	
Genitive	inferiorum	inferiorum	

9. Prefixes

Prefixes	Meaning	Derivatives
ab-, a-, abs-	from, away from	aboral
*ad-	to, toward, near	adoral
ambi-, amb-, ambo-	around, on both sides	ambilateral
ante-	before, in front of	anteflect
antero-	before, prior	anteromedial
circum-	around	circumflex
com-, co-, col-, con-, cor-	with, together	complicate
contra-	against, opposite	contraception
de-	down, from, away	dejection
dis-, di-, dif-	apart, not	disjunction
ex-, e-, ef-	out, out of, from	express
extra-	beyond, outside	extracorporeal
in-, im-, ir-	in, into, upon	incorporate
in-, il-, im-, ir-	not	inactive
infra-	below, under	infracostal
inter-	between, among	intergemmal
intra-, intro-	within, inside, inward	introversion
juxta-	near, next to	juxtaposition
non-	not	nonconductor
ob-, o-, oc-, of-, op-	before, against	objective
per-	through, throughout	perflation
post-	behind, after	postnatal
postero-	behind	posterotemporal
prae-, pre-	before, ahead	premature
pro-	before, in front of, forward	projection
re-, red-	back, again	remit

retro-	backward, behind	*retronasal*
se-	apart, without	*secure*
semi-	half	*semiflexion*
sub-, suc-, suf-, sup-, sus-	under, less than, deficient	*subnasal*
super, supra-	over, above, excessive	*supercilium*
trans-, tra-	across, through	*transocular*
ultra-	beyond, excessive	*ultrasonic*

* Often assimilated to a following consonant. The adverbial suffix *-ad* also means to or toward: caud*ad*.

10. Suffixes

English	Latin	Meaning	English	Latin
-able	-abilis, -e	able to be, worthy of	*honorable*	*honorabilis*
-ible	-ibilis, -e		*flexible*	*flexibilis*
-aceous	-aceus, -a, -um	pertaining to	*herbaceous*	*herbaceus*
-acy	-acia	quality of, state, rank, office	*efficacy*	*efficacia*
-al	-alis, -e	pertaining or belonging to	*nasal*	*nasalis*
-an	-anus, -a, -um	pertaining to	*Roman*	*Romanus*
-ance	-antia	quality, condition,	*tolerance*	*tolerantia*
-ancy	-antia	state, or result of	*constancy*	*constantia*
-ence	-entia		*convenience*	*convenientia*
-ency	-entia		*fluency*	*fluentia*
-ant	-antem	one who, that which,	*servant*	*servantem*
-ent	-entem	act or process of	*fluent*	*fluentem*
			ambulant	*ambulantem*
-ar	-aris, -e	pertaining to or like	*regular*	*regularis*
-ary	-arius, -a, -um		*secondary*	*secundarius*
-ory	-orius, -a, -um		*auditory*	*auditorius*
-arium	-arium	place where	*aquarium*	*aquarium*
-ary	-arium		*aviary*	*aviarium*
-orium	-orium		*sensorium*	*sensorium*
-ory	-orium		*dormitory*	*dormitorium*
-ate	-atus, -a, -um	having, provided with	*barbate*	*barbatus*
-atic	-aticus, -a, -um	pertaining to	*aquatic*	*aquaticus*
-ic	-icus, -a, -um		*lyric*	*lyricus*
-ation	-atio	act, state, condition,	*radiation*	*radiatio*
-ion	-io	process, or result of	*revision*	*revisio*
-ative	-ativus, -a, -um	tending to, relating to,	*laxative*	*laxativus*
-ive	-ivus, -a, -um	belonging to, or connected with	*active*	*activus*
-cle	-culus, -a, -um	diminutive	*ventricle*	*ventriculus*
-cule	-culus, -a, -um		*molecule*	*moleculus*
-icle	-iculus, -a, -um		*particle*	*particula*

-ole	-olus, -a, -um		*aureole*	*aureolus*
-ule	-ulus, -a, -um		*cellule*	*cellula*
-er		one who or that which	*divider*	
-or	-or		*actor*	*actor*
-ety	-etas	quality, condition, or	*piety*	*pietas*
-ity	-itas	state of	*felicity*	*felicitas*
-ty	-tas		*liberty*	*libertas*
-eous	-eus, -a, -um	belonging to or made of	*corneous*	*corneus*
-ia	-ia	quality, condition, or state of	*dementia*	*dementia*
-id	-idus, -a, -um	pertaining to	*morbid*	*morbidus*
-ile	-ilis, -e	pertaining to or capable of	*fertile*	*fertilis*
-il	-ilis, -e		*civil*	*civilis*
-ine	-inus, -a, -um	pertaining to or like	*feline*	*felinus*
-lent	-lentus, -a, -um	full of	*corpulent*	*corpulentus*
-ment	-mentum	result, act, or means of	*rudiment*	*rudimentum*
-mentum	-mentum		*momentum*	*momentum*
-ose	-osus, -a, -um	pertaining to, having	*verbose*	*verbosus*
-ous	-osus, -a, -um	the quality of, or full of	*copious*	*copiosus*
-tude	-tudo	condition or state of	*multitude*	*multitudo*
-ure	-ura	process, state, act, or result of	*fracture*	*fractura*

Notes:

LESSON I

11. Vocabulary

lac, lactis, *n.:* milk
latus, -eris, *n.:* side
cibus, -i, *m.:* food
morbus, -i, *m.:* disease, sickness
somnus, -i, *m.:* sleep
claudico, *pp.* **-atus,** v.: to limp
bursa, -ae, *f.:* purse (sac)
lingua, -ae, *f.:* tongue
cornu, -us, *n.:* horn
copia, -ae, *f.:* plenty
fistula, -ae, *f.:* pipe, tube
traho, *pp.* **tractus,** v.: to draw
flo, *pp.* **-atus,** v.: to blow
tempus, -oris, *n.:* time, temple of the head
occiput, -itis, *n.:* back of the head
fero, *pp.* **latus,** v.: to bear, carry
bene, adv.: well
papilla, -ae, *f.:* nipple; dim. of *papula,* pimple

sudor, -oris, *m.:* sweat
facio (**-fac, -fic, -fice,** and **-fy** *are variant English bases of* **facio**), *pp.* **factus,** (**-fect**), v.: to do, build, make
ambulo, *pp.* **-atus,** v.: to walk
alveus, -i, *m.:* cavity
posterior, -oris, comp. adj.: after, behind (time or place)
anterior, -oris, comp. adj.: before (time or place)
commissura, -ae, *f.:* seam, joining together
funis, -is, *m.:* cord, rope
emulgeo, *pp.* **emulsus,** v.: to drain, milk out
superior, -oris, comp. adj.: farther above, upper
male, adv.: badly, ill
digitus, -i, *m.:* finger, toe

12. Define etymologically:

digit	subtraction	superiority
somnolent	commissural	effect
inflator	lacteal	morbid
occipitotemporal	claudication	sudorific
posterolateral	alveolus	postcibal
cornual	temporal	bursal
lactimorbus	digital	papilliferous
papule	retrolingual	papuliferous
ambulant	posteriority	lactic
insufflation	funic	cornification
digitation	inflation	somnambulance
subcontract	extract	temporary
morbidity	traction	lactiferous
funicular	lingual	emulgent
posterosuperior	sudoriferous	insomnia
occipital	extraction	benefactor
factor	papillate	intractable
papillary	infect	lateral
cornucopia	ambulatory	referable

Notes:

LESSON I

13. Indicate the meaning suggested by the following prefixes:

1. post-	2. ultra-	3. co-	4. inter-	5. per-
6. ab-	7. ante-	8. ex-	9. re-	10. antero-
11. pro-	12. retro-	13. sup-	14. non-	15. dif-

14. List the prefixes which may be used to indicate the following meanings:

1. below	2. around	3. under	4. beyond	5. across
6. over	7. through	8. with	9. behind	10. down

15. Indicate the meaning suggested by the following suffixes:

1. -ate	2. -ible	3. -ory	4. -lent	5. -ure
6. -ic	7. -ive	8. -tude	9. -cle	10. -al

16. Using a standard medical dictionary, find the exact medical meaning, and indicate the pronunciation, of each of the following words:

1. cornucopia	2. emulsion	3. bursa
4. funiculus	5. fistula	6. commissure

17. Accent the penult of the following Latin words:

1. sagitta	2. placenta	3. papilla	4. omnis
5. nevus	6. internus	7. pectus	8. pulsus

18. Supply the genitive singular form of each of these Latin words:

1. lac	2. superior	3. copia	4. latus
5. funis	6. bursa	7. papula	8. sudor

19. Match the columns by placing the correct numbers in the second column before each English meaning in the first column:

......ill	1. papilla
......nipple	2. fistula
......tongue	3. morbus
......pipe	4. male
......sickness	5. lingua

Notes:

LESSON II

20. Vocabulary

dulcis, -e, adj.: sweet
oculus, -i, m.: eye
os, oris, n.: mouth
dexter, -tra, -trum, adj.: right
nasus, -i, m.: nose
febris, -is, f.: fever
caput, -itis, n.: head
fenestra, -ae, f.: window
fovea, -ae, f.: pit
fluo, pp. fluxus, v.: to flow
mala, -ae, f.: cheek, cheekbone
purus, -a, -um, adj.: pure
lacrima, -ae, f.: tear
fossa, -ae, f.: ditch, trench
lacto, pp. -atus, v.: to suckle
misceo, pp. mixtus, v.: to mix

partus, -us, m.: birth
paries, -etis, m.: wall
auris, -is, f.: ear
cubitum, -i, n.: elbow
inferior, -oris, comp. adj.: below, lower
foramen, -inis, n.: aperture
facies, -ei, f.: face
circus, -i, m.: circle
palpebra, -ae, f.: eyelid
aqua, -ae, f.: water
femur, -oris or -inis, n.: thigh
sanguis, -inis, m.: blood
tergeo, pp. tersus, v.: to wipe
corpus, -oris, n.: body, mass
figo, pp. fixus, v.: to fasten

21. Define etymologically:

circumferential
purify
ambidexter
circular
postocular
aquatic
antecubital
capitular
mixture
conflation
foraminiferous
facial
foveola
aquosity
papillose
detergent
antero-inferior
antefebrile
sanguineous
corporal
fixation

lactation
miscible
aurinasal
influx
corpulent
ambilateral
sublingual
contralateral
aqueous
sanguiferous
dextraural
confluent
circumoral
adoral
purification
insufflate
sanguinolent
palpebral
dulcify
auriculotemporal
transference

febrific
corniculate
faciolingual
fluent
circumfluent
lacrimal
aquiferous
aboral
sanguification
dextrocular
anterolateral
parietal
palpebrate
lacrimation
miscibility
subfacial
malar
dexterity
circumambulate
corpuscle
fixative

22. Give the medical definition of each of the following words:

1. fossa
2. femur
3. papilla
4. febricula
5. fenestra
6. paries
7. fovea
8. corpus

Notes:

LESSON II

23. Memorize the following common Latin terms, phrases, and abbreviations which are frequently used in prescriptions:

Term or Phrase	Abbreviation	Meaning
aqua	aq.	water
cum aqua	cum aq.	with water
ex aqua	ex aq.	with water
in aqua	in aq.	in water
sine aqua	sin. aq.	without water
pilula; pilulae	pil.	pill; pills
divide; dividatur	div.	divide
numero	no.	number
massa	mass.	mass
pasta	past.	paste
misce	M.	mix
solutio	sol.	solution
emplastrum	emp.	plaster
lotio	lot.	lotion

24. State the Latin rule of accent.

25. Supply the meanings and the verbal bases of these Latin verbs:

1. fluo	2. emulgeo	3. misceo	4. fero
5. flo	6. ambulo	7. traho	8. tergeo

26. Indicate the meaning of each of the following prefixes and suffixes:

1. -eus	2. -ule	3. inter-	4. -ancy	5. ultra-
6. super-	7. -or	8. -ine	9. pre-	10. se-

27. Accent the antepenult of the following words:

1. lenticular	2. retractable	3. incipient
4. compressibility	5. tibiofemoral	6. infanticide
7. vivisectorium	8. nervimotility	9. aquarium

28. Translate:

1. **Divide massam in pilulas xxx.**
2. **Misce cum aqua.**
3. **Div. in pil. xx.**
4. **M. past. in aqua.**

Notes:

LESSON III

29. Vocabulary

nuntius (nuncius), -i, *m.:* messenger
lens, lentis, *f.:* lentil (lens)
porta, -ae, *f.:* gate
pario, *pp.* paritus *or* partus, v.: to bear
cauda, -ae, *f.:* tail
sagitta, -ae, *f.:* arrow
fundo, *pp.* fusus, v.: to pour
conus, -i, *m.:* cone
flecto, *pp.* flexus, v.: to bend
meatus, -us, *m.:* going, passage, course
ren, renis, *m.:* kidney
pars, partis, *f.:* part
cutis, -is, *f.:* skin
sternum, -i, *n.:* chest

premo, *pp.* pressus, v.: to press
cuneus, -i, *m.:* wedge
ruber, -bra, -brum, adj.: red
duco, *pp.* ductus, v.: to draw, lead
ductus, -us, *m.:* duct, canal
forma, -ae, *f.:* form
pannus, -i, *m.:* cloth
parturio, *pp.* parturitus, v.: to be in labor
glomus, -eris, *n.:* skein, clew
dorsum, -i, *n.:* back
luna, -ae, *f.:* moon
venter, -tris, *m.:* belly
rostrum, -i, *n.:* beak
ovum, -i, *n.:* egg
sinister, -tra, -trum, adj.: left

30. Define etymologically:

contrary
meatal
dorsoanterior
cuneiform
inflexion
dorsolateral
infusion
nonconductor
ventral
reflex
ventrodorsad
parturifacient
aqueduct
oviduct
internuncial
rostriform
particle
sagittal
ventrad
expresser
oviparous

compress
lunar
juxtaglomerular
ventriduct
ovule
retrosternal
subcuticular
rubefacient
lunatic
semilunar
reniform
sinistraural
refusion
lentiform
parturition
reflect
dorsiduct
sinister
dorsad
palpebration
superfluous

retractable
lenticonus
rostral
renal
induce
subdorsal
transfusion
ovary
ventricular
reflector
lenticular
cuticle
subduct
caudad
oviform
glomerule
reniportal
repressive
interparietal
funiform
caudate

Notes:

LESSON III

31. Translate the following Latin phrases:

1. palpebra superior
2. meatus nasi
3. pars nasalis
4. pars sinistra
5. latus dextrum
6. palpebra inferior
7. cibus purus
8. aqua dulcis
9. funiculus anterior
10. fovea capitis femoris

32. List the prefixes which may be used to indicate the following meanings:

1. on
2. half
3. together
4. under
5. toward
6. again
7. apart
8. around
9. against
10. behind
11. within
12. beyond

33. Supply one meaning for each of the following suffixes:

1. -ic
2. -al
3. -er
4. -cle
5. -tude
6. -lent
7. -ive
8. -id
9. -ure
10. -ancy
11. -orium
12. -ar
13. -ate
14. -an
15. -aceus

34. List two or more English derivatives from each of the following Latin words:

1. **pus, puris,** *n.:* corrupt matter, pus
2. **solvo,** *pp.* **solutus,** v.: to loosen, set free
3. **acer, acris, acre,** adj.: sharp, pointed, cutting
4. **cludo,** *pp.* **clusus,** v.: to close, shut
5. **rete, -is,** *n.:* net

35. Give the Latin term and the English meaning for each of the following abbreviations used in prescriptions:

1. aq.
2. M.
3. past.
4. in aq.
5. sol.
6. emp.

36. Supply the meaning of each of the following past participles:

1. fusus
2. tersus
3. tractus
4. factus
5. latus
6. flexus
7. pressus
8. mixtus

Notes:

LESSON IV

37. Vocabulary

jacio, *pp.* jactus (-ject), v.: to throw
scapula, -ae, *f.:* shoulder blade
pulmo, -onis, *m.:* lungs
ausculto, *pp.* -atus, v.: to listen to
vesica, -ae, *f.:* bladder
ligo, *pp.* -atus, v.: to bind, tie
spina, -ae, *f.:* thorn, spine, backbone
fascis, -is, *m.:* bundle
humerus, -i, *m.:* shoulder
verus, -a, -um, adj.: true
locus, -i, *m.:* place
loco, *pp.* -atus, v.: to place
ulna, -ae, *f.:* elbow, arm
signo, *pp.* -atus, v.: to set a mark upon, write
signum, -i, *n.:* mark, sign
vir, -i, *m.:* man

longissimus, -a, -um, sup. adj.: longest
costa, -ae, *f.:* rib
longus, -a, -um, adj.: long
medicus, -a, -um, adj.: pertaining to healing
audio, *pp.* auditus, v.: to hear
viscus, -eris, *n.:* internal organs
inguen, -inis, *n.:* groin
carpus, -i, *m.:* wrist
medius, -a, -um, adj.: middle
manus, -us, *f.:* hand
cervix, -icis, *f.:* neck
lumbus, -i, *m.:* loin
ilium, -i, *n.:* hipbone
spicio, *pp.* spectus, v.: to look, see
scribo, *pp.* scriptus, v.: to write
et, conj.: and

38. Define etymologically:

costoscapular
prescription
viscerad
fascicle
costoinferior
intrarenal
virile
signify
medical
ilioinguinal
inspection
inscribe
lumbocostal
virility
intercostal
introspection
interdigital
dislocate
ulnad
extrapulmonary

subscribe
mediad
iliocostal
ulnar
significator
humeral
iliolumbar
medicornu
vesicle
ventrolateral
ulnocarpal
ligature
auscultation
injection
manual
costosternal
cervical
audile
description
ligation

mediolateral
costiform
retronasal
infrascapular
prerenal
collateral
medioccipital
retrojection
audition
cervicofacial
affusion
oval
visceroparietal
humeroscapular
purify
sinistrocular
iliofemoral
fasciculation
pulmonary
significance

Notes:

LESSON IV

39. Explain the following medical terms:

1. gustatory audition
3. intercuneiform ligaments

2. immediate auscultation
4. manus flexa

40. Supply the perfect participle passive and give the English meaning of each of the following Latin verbs:

1. flecto
4. tergeo
7. facio
10. cludo

2. traho
5. fluo
8. flo
11. scribo

3. ambulo
6. misceo
9. solvo
12. ausculto

41. Memorize the following common Latin expressions and abbreviations found in the subscriptions and *signa* of prescriptions:

Term or Phrase	Abbreviation	Meaning
ana	aa.	of each
emulsum	emul.	emulsion
unguentum	ungt.	ointment
filtra	filt.	filter
linimentum	lin.	liniment
capiat	cap.	let him take
fiat; fiant	ft.	let it be made; let them be made
ante cibos	a.c.	before meals
post cibos	p.c.	after meals
adde; addatur	add.	add; let be added
absente febre	abs. feb.	fever being absent
tabella; tabellae	tab.	tablet; tablets
gutta; guttae	gtt.	drop; drops

42. Supply three or more English words derived from each of these Latin words:

1. **doceo,** *pp.* **doctus,** v.: to teach, instruct
2. **tolero,** *pp.* **toleratus,** v.: to bear, endure
3. **curo,** *pp.* **curatus,** v.: to take care of, see to

43. Translate:

1. **Capiat guttas x ante cibos.**
2. **Divide in tabellas.**
3. **Fiat unguentum.**
4. **Capiat pilulas cum aqua.**
5. **Add. lin.**

Notes:

LESSON V

44. Vocabulary

virus, -i, n.: poison
radix, -icis, f.: root
mens, mentis, f.: mind
genu, pl. genua, n.: knee
pluma, -ae, f.: feather
dens, dentis, m.: tooth
fibra, -ae, f.: fiber
servo, pp. -atus, v.: to save, keep
rumpo, pp. ruptus, v.: to break, burst
labium, -i, n.: lip
equus, -i, m.: horse
sura, -ae, f.: calf of the leg
frango, pp. fractus, v.: to break
capio (cipi), pp. captus (cept), v.: to take, seize
laxo, pp. -atus, v.: to loosen

os, ossis, n.: bone
mentum, -i, n.: chin
sacer, -cra, -crum, adj.: sacred, holy
sol, solis, m.: sun
hospes, -itis, m. or f.: guest, host
frons, frontis, f.: forehead, front
cor, cordis, n.: heart
pono, pp. positus, v.: to place
macero, pp. -atus, v.: to soften, soak
filum, -i, n.: thread
tendo, pp. tentus or tensus, v.: to stretch
mamma, -ae, f.: breast
coxa, -ae, f.: hip, hip joint
dispenso, pp. -atus, v.: to distribute by weight
plico, pp. -atus, v.: to fold

45. Define etymologically:

sural	sinistrad	ossicle
equine	rupture	indentation
labial	maceration	submammary
disposer	mentality	suppository
beneceptor	eruption	filiform
sinistrality	fragile	denture
position	genuflect	solar
coxal	cordiform	radiciform
refraction	preservative	inception
coxofemoral	supragenual	fracture
labionasal	tension	preservability
mammiform	conception	intraspinal
virulent	intension	corruption
interdental	solarium	incipient
radical	retromammary	component
virose	hospital	filoplume
mental	prefrontal	superscription
abducent	ossify	ossiferous
dispensary	signate	compressibility
ligament	suprasternal	iliospinal
collocate	costosuperior	receptor
laxative	complication	laxator

Notes:

LESSON V

46. Translate the following Latin phrases:

1. cauda equina	2. costarum longarum
3. aqua pura	4. radix nasi
5. spina nasalis anterior	6. costa vera
7. spina nasalis	8. manus et carpus
9. febris rubra	10. os costale
11. radix posterior	12. radix dentis
13. auris media	14. manus sinistra

47. List three or more English derivatives from each of the following Latin words:

1. **jungo,** *pp.* **junctus,** v.: to join, unite, connect
2. **quantus, -a, -um,** adj.: how much, how many
3. **mel, mellis,** *n.:* honey
4. **mensis, -is,** *m.:* month
5. **albus, -a, -um,** adj.: white
6. **lenis, -e,** adj.: gentle, mild

48. Supply the genitive singular form and the meaning of each of these Latin words:

1. dens	2. filum	3. bursa	4. latus
5. funis	6. oculus	7. morbus	8. sudor
9. auris	10. os	11. caput	12. venter

49. Using a standard medical dictionary, find the exact medical definition of each of the following Latin words:

1. sacrum	2. filum	3. labium
4. foramen	5. radix	6. funis

50. Give the Latin term and the English meaning of each of these abbreviations:

1. cum aq.	2. p.c.	3. filt.	4. ft.
5. mass.	6. aa.	7. abs. feb.	8. ungt.
9. a.c.	10. tab.	11. past.	12. sol.

Notes:

LESSON VI

51. Vocabulary

bacillus, -i, m.: rod
bacca, -ae, f.: berry
findo, pp. fissus, v.: to split, divide
seta, -ae, f.: bristle
herba, -ae, f.: herb
vas, vasis, n.: vessel
cavus, -a, -um, adj.: hollow, concave
foro, pp. -atus, v.: to bore
velum, -i, n.: veil, sail
lignum, -i, n.: wood
cera, -ae, f.: wax
lobus, -i, m.: lobe of the ear
vena, -ae, f.: vein
divido, pp. divisus, v.: to divide, separate
cilium, -i, n.: eyelid
bini, -ae, -a, adj.: two by two

gusto, pp. -atus, v.: to taste
acidus, -a, -um, adj.: sour
acetum, -i, n.: vinegar
carbo, -onis, m.: coal
maxilla, -ae, f.: jawbone
urina, -ae, f.: urine
moveo, pp. motus, v.: to move
tego, pp. tectus, v.: to cover
voro, pp. -atus, v.: to devour, eat
bucca, -ae, f.: cheek
callus, -i, m.: hard skin
lupus, -i, m.: wolf
maximus, -a, -um, sup. adj.: greatest
scindo, pp. scissus, v.: to cut, tear, split
indico, pp. -atus, v.: to point out

52. Define etymologically:

ceriferous	preoral	preinduction
dispenser	division	vasoformative
callosity	bacillus	pressure
lobule	buccal	bacillar
retrocervical	setiferous	buccilingual
rejection	herbivorous	gustation
acid	protection	acetify
inguinal	uriniferous	fission
frontal	scissors	vasomotorial
gustatory	acidity	urinary
vascular	infusible	cavity
scissure	bacciform	callous
medial	acetic	integument
local	maximal	insusceptibility
superciliary	scission	retrobuccal
suprascapular	perforation	osseous
uriniparous	fissure	dorsoventrad
maxillodental	venose	ligniform
herbarium	inframammary	parietooccipital
vasiform	fascicular	expressible
dividable	dispensation	submaxillary
juxtaposition	oviferous	irremovability
gustable	commove	lignify
recombinant	predisposition	transpose

Notes:

LESSON VI

53. Memorize the following Latin terms, abbreviations, and meanings:

Term or Phrase	Abbreviation	Meaning
dispensa; dispensetur	disp.	dispense
admove; admoveatur	admov.	apply; let be applied
dolore urgenta	dol. urg.	while pain lasts
drachma; drachmae	3	a drachm; drachms
uncia	3	an ounce
statim	stat.	immediately
capsula; capsulae	cap.	capsule; capsules
suppositorium; suppositoria	suppos.	suppository; suppositories

54. Translate the following Latin terms:

1. velum interpositum
2. carbo ligni
3. copia cerae
4. lobus occipitalis
5. lobus temporalis
6. ligamentum inguinale
7. superior maxilla
8. urina cibi
9. morbus coxae
10. cor mobile

55. Supply a complete definition of each of these medical words:

1. lupus
2. bacillus
3. seta
4. cauda
5. meatus
6. glomus

56. State the approximate location of the following veins:

1. venae vesicales
2. venae spinales
3. venae labiales inferiores
4. vena occipitalis
5. venae cordis anteriores
6. vena lingualis
7. venae dorsales linguae
8. vena lobi medii
9. vena pulmonalis superior dextra
10. vena intercostalis superior sinistra

57. Indicate the form, shape, or likeness indicated by each of the following words:

1. reniform
2. bacciform
3. rostriform
4. vasiform
5. funiform
6. setiform
7. oviform
8. ligniform
9. lentiform

Notes:

LESSON VII

58. Vocabulary

veho, *pp.* **vectus,** v.: to carry, bear, draw
oleum, -i, *n.:* oil
furca, -ae, *f.:* fork
nervus, -i, *m.:* nerve
alo, *pp.* alitus *or* altus, v.: to nourish
argentum, -i, *n.:* silver
cresco, *pp.* **cretus,** v.: to grow
niger, -ra, -rum, adj.: black
bis (bi-), adv.: twice

dies, -ei, *f.:* day
hernia, -ae, *f.:* rupture
norma, -ae, *f.:* rule, pattern
ago, *pp.* **actus,** v.: to do, perform, make
cubo (cubit), v.: to lie in bed
gero, *pp.* **gestus,** v.: to bear
ter, adv.: three times
quater, adv.: four times
omnis, -e, adj.: all, every
hora, -ae, *f.:* hour

59. Cardinal and Ordinal Numerals

unus, -a, -um: one
duo, duae, duo: two
tres, tria: three
quattuor: four
quinque: five
sex: six
septem: seven
octo: eight
novem: nine
decem: ten
centum: one hundred
mille: one thousand

primus, -a, -um, adj.: first
secundus, -a, -um, adj.: second
tertius, -a, -um, adj.: third
quartus, -a, -um, adj.: fourth
quintus, -a, -um, adj.: fifth
sextus, -a, -um, adj.: sixth
septimus, -a, -um, adj.: seventh
octavus, -a, -um, adj.: eighth
nonus, -a, -um, adj.: ninth
decimus, -a, -um, adj.: tenth

60. Define etymologically:

concrete	primary	union
bilateral	oleic	preparation
cervicolingual	hernial	trilobate
reaction	inscription	dentigerous
sacrospinal	denticle	biforate
ingestion	unicorn	alimentary
subnormality	agent	nervimotility
interaction	unicostate	uniform
crescent	omniferous	vectorial
secondary	congestion	unilobar
uniforate	normal	trimanual
action	unify	lactigerous
bifurcate	herniation	argentine
contraction	introflection	recombination
transposition	contraceptive	contraception

Notes:

LESSON VII

61. Give the approximate location of the following nerves:

1. nervus mentalis
3. nervus lumboinguinalis
5. nervus lingualis
7. nervus suralis

2. nervus intercostohumeralis
4. nervus femoralis
6. nervi digitales dorsales
8. nervus maxillaris

62. State the exact scientific definition of each of the following medical terms:

1. decubital
4. quintipara

2. hernia
5. octarius

3. sextan
6. furcula

63. Memorize the following common Latin expressions and abbreviations found in the subscriptions and *signa* of prescriptions:

Term or Phrase	Abbreviation	Meaning
signa; signetur	Sig.	write; let be written
pro re nata	p.r.n.	as the occasion arises
bis in die	b.i.d.	twice a day
ter in die	t.i.d.	three times a day
quater in die	q.i.d.	four times a day
omni secunda hora	omn. 2 hr.	every second hour
omni tertia hora	omn. tert. hr.	every third hour
centum	C.	one hundred
de die in diem	de d. in di.	from day to day
dentur tales doses	d.t.d.	give of such doses
non repetatur	non rep.	do not repeat
ut dictum	ut dict.	as directed

64. Indicate one meaning for each of these Latin prefixes and suffixes:

1. -aris
6. -tudo
11. semi-

2. inter-
7. -alis
12. de-

3. -mentum
8. -entia
13. sub-

4. -or
9. ex-
14. di-

5. juxta-
10. -ura
15. -ilis

65. Translate the following Latin terms:

1. bucca cava
4. lac acidum

2. fovea submaxillaris
5. norma occipitalis

3. cera auris
6. palpebra tertia

Notes:

LESSON VIII

REVIEW

66. Supply a Latin prefix or suffix for each of the following:

1. half	....	2. full of	....
3. one who	....	4. apart	....
5. below	....	6. not	....
7. able to be	....	8. place where	....
9. between	....	10. result of	....
11. provided with	....	12. with	....
13. beyond	....	14. tending to	....

67. Provide a Latin word for each of the following terms:

1. disease	....	2. long	....
3. kidney	....	4. blood	....
5. mouth	....	6. tongue	....
7. chest	....	8. belly	....
9. to tie	....	10. to write	....
11. to nourish	....	12. to divide	....
13. eyelid	....	14. vinegar	....

68. Supply the meanings of the following Latin words:

1. **oleum**	....	2. **latus**	....
3. **vas**	....	4. **ulna**	....
5. **filum**	....	6. **cauda**	....
7. **inguen**	....	8. **norma**	....
9. **cubitum**	....	10. **copia**	....
11. **oculus**	....	12. **dens**	....
13. **dorsum**	....	14. **acidus**	....

69. Give the combining forms of the following Latin nouns:

1. **ovum**	....	2. **cor**	....
3. **hospes**	....	4. **foramen**	....
5. **lacrima**	....	6. **pulmo**	....
7. **bacillus**	....	8. **velum**	....
9. **lac**	....	10. **sol**	....

70. Supply the perfect passive participle of each of the following Latin verbs:

1. **premo**	....	2. **facio**	....
3. **audio**	....	4. **moveo**	....
5. **pono**	....	6. **tergeo**	....

71. Provide the Latin abbreviation and meaning of each of the following pharmaceutical terms or phrases:

1. **absente febre**	....	....
2. **numero**	....	....
3. **cum aqua**	....	....
4. **admoveatur**	....	....
5. **capsulae**	....	....

REVIEW

6. **ante cibos**   . . . .
7. **uncia**   . . . .

72. Translate into Latin:

1. Divide the mass into twenty tablets.   . . . .
   . . . .
2. Take one pill with water.   . . . .
   . . . .
3. Let him take an ounce immediately before meals.   . . . .
   . . . .
4. Apply the liniment while the pain lasts.   . . . .
   . . . .
5. Add a drachm.   . . . .
   . . . .

73. Define etymologically:

1. ambilateral . . . .
2. circumocular . . . .
3. inframammary . . . .
4. postcordial . . . .
5. transfusion . . . .
6. aboral . . . .
7. extrabuccal . . . .
8. intracorporeal . . . .
9. adduction . . . .
10. intensity . . . .
11. femoral . . . .
12. antecubital . . . .
13. profundity . . . .
14. linguiform . . . .
15. semiconductor . . . .
16. transduction . . . .
17. juxtaposition . . . .
18. reniportal . . . .
19. prescriptive . . . .
20. humeroscapular . . . .
    . . . .

LESSON IX

74. Vocabulary

vertebra, -ae, *f.*: joint, vertebra of the spine
pelvis, -is, *f.*: basin
arbor, -oris, *f.*: tree
guttur, -uris, *n.*: throat
uva, -ae, *f.*: grape
tibia, -ae, *f.*: shinbone
verto (vorto), *pp.* versus, v.: to turn
plumbum, -i, *n.*: lead
cloaca, -ae, *f.*: sewer
talus, -i, *m.*: ankle, anklebone
cerebrum, -i, *n.*: brain
colo, *pp.* cultus, v.: to take care of, cultivate

sulcus, -i, *m.*: ditch, trench
puer, pueri, *m.*: boy
pectus, -oris, *n.*: breast, breastbone
membrana, -ae, *f.*: skin
caedo (cid), *pp.* caesus (cis), v.: to cut, kill, destroy
gyrus, -i, *m.*: circle
vacca, -ae, *f.*: cow
fibula, -ae, *f.*: clasp, pin, buckle
certus, -a, -um, adj.: certain, sure
pes, pedis, *m.*: foot
coquo, *pp.* coctus, v.: to boil
infans, infantis, *m.* or *f.*: infant

75. Define etymologically:

divisibility
circumcision
infantile
eversion
lumbar
labiodental
uviform
taliped
vertebrarium
cerebellar
infanticide
introversion
talofibular
subtegumental
invert
puerculture
seduction
sternovertebral
acidify
vasal
nigritude
iliotibial
certifiable
versatility

vertebrate
cerebral
certitude
subjection
tibial
relative
certify
puerile
tibiofemoral
membrane
incisor
transfer
incision
sudoral
cerebrospinal
sacrad
transverse
supramental
divider
sacral
furcate
intervertebral
infantile
replicate

repression
pectoral
concoction
puerperal
visceral
receptor
sudatorium
sulciform
decoction
interfemoral
supramaxillary
frontonasal
plumbic
controverter
talotibial
guttural
tibiad
cavitary
signature
decimal
reverse
cultural
concise
implication

Notes:

LESSON IX

76. Supply the abbreviations and English meanings of the following Latin terms used in prescriptions:

1. fiat	2. post cibos	3. divide
4. dispensa	5. signetur	6. misce
7. ter in die	8. omni secunda hora	9. non repetatur
10. pilula	11. tabella	12. de die in diem
13. solutio	14. fiant	15. addatur

77. List two or more English words which have been derived from each of the following Latin nouns:

1. clavis, -is, *f.:* key
2. clava, -ae, *f.:* club
3. falx, falcis, *f.:* sickle, scythe
4. floccus, -i, *m.:* tuft of wool
5. radius, -i, *m.:* ray, rod
6. petra, -ae, *f.:* rock, stone

78. Match the columns by placing the correct numbers in the second column before each term in the first column:

..... costosuperior
..... sinistromanual
..... subcostal
..... submaxillary
..... palpebration
..... buccolingual
..... medial
..... lupine
..... funic
..... venose
..... sinistrocular

1. pertaining to the center
2. beneath the ribs
3. winking
4. wolfish
5. pertaining to the umbilical cord
6. left-eyed
7. relating to the upper ribs
8. pertaining to cheek and tongue
9. left-handed
10. beneath the lower jaw
11. having veins

79. Translate:

1. Admov. lin. p.r.n. dol. urg.
2. Cap. cum aq. ut dict. b.i.d.
3. M. Ft. lot. Sig.:Admov. lot. q.i.d.
4. Capiat pilulam unam ex aqua.

Notes:

LESSON X

80. Vocabulary

major, -oris, comp. adj.: greater
minor, -oris, comp. adj.: lesser
totus, -a, -um, adj.: all
dolor, -oris, *m.:* pain
externus, -a, -um, adj.: external
internus, -a, -um, adj.: inner
brevis, -e, adj.: short
video, *pp.* **visus,** v.: to see
levigo, *pp.* **-atus,** v.: to make smooth
moneo, *pp.* **monitus,** v.: to warn
ulcus, -eris, *n.:* sore, ulcer
lino, *pp.* **litus,** v.: to smear upon
lumbricus, -i, *m.:* worm
proximus, -a, -um, sup. adj.: next
dico, *pp.* **dictus,** v.: to speak, say

gingiva, -ae, *.f:* gum
vitrum, -i, *n.:* glass
vitreus, -a, -um, adj.: glassy
lamina, -ae, *f.:* thin plate, flat layer
maturo, *pp.* **-atus,** v.: to ripen
operor, *pp.* **-atus,** v.: to work
cancer, -cri, *m.:* crab, cancer
potens, -entis, adj.: powerful
paro, *pp.* **-atus,** v.: to prepare, get ready
murus, -i, *m.:* wall
sto (stat), v.: to stand
lumen, -inis, *n.:* light
mus, muris, *m.* or *f.:* mouse
musculus, -i, *m.:* muscle

81. Define etymologically:

frontal	reception	suppressor
proximal	lamination	majority
luminiferous	liniment	arboriculture
impotent	muscle	preparation
operation	linguogingival	provisional
maturity	contrast	approximation
monitor	distal	gingival
proximobuccal	extramural	murine
subdorsal	caudal	portal
fragility	centipede	totalitarian
luminous	ulceration	prepotency
preparator	vitrify	lumbricide
maturation	brevity	total
intramuscular	vitreodentine	levigation
visible	minority	inoperative
intramural	laminar	vitrifacture
stable	premonitory	proximolabial
muscularity	instability	frontomalar
sternal	vertebrofemoral	substance
aliment	infancy	proximity
herbarium	dolorific	nervine
commotion	lignification	quartisternal
abnormality	concision	revert

Notes:

LESSON X

82. Supply the verbal bases and give the English meaning of each of these Latin verbs:

1. ausculto	2. audio	3. scindo	4. rumpo
5. dispenso	6. caedo	7. frango	8. ago
9. ligo	10. scribo	11. veho	12. paro
13. moneo	14. foro	15. pono	16. findo

83. Memorize the following Latin terms, abbreviations, and English meanings:

Term or Phrase	Abbreviation	Meaning
omni die	o.d.	daily
omni nocte	o.n.	every night
omni mane	o.m.	every morning
hora somni	h.s.	at bedtime
ad libitum	ad lib.	at pleasure
dosis; doses	dos.	a dose; doses
trochiscus; trochisci	troch.	a lozenge; lozenges
si opus sit	s.o.s.	if necessary
pone	—	place; put
mistura	mist.	mixture

84. Translate these medical terms:

1. morbus pedis
2. lamina prevertebralis
3. auris externa
4. sulci cutis
5. facies inferior linguae
6. vasa auris internae
7. hora quinta
8. membrana cordis
9. nervi cervicales
10. vertebrae verae

85. List and translate the Latin names of fifteen individual muscles.

86. Translate into Latin:

1. Let a mixture be made.
2. Take as directed as the occasion arises.
3. Write: Take one tablet with water after meals.
4. Dispense an ounce of the mixture.
5. Take three times a day.

Notes:

LESSON XI

87. Vocabulary

tussis, -is, f.: cough
nox, noctis, f.: night
pons, pontis, m.: bridge
abdomen, -inis, n.: belly
unguis, -is, m.: nail
pilus, -i, m.: hair
corium, -i, n.: leather, skin, hide
palatum, -i, n.: palate
ramus, -i, m.: branch
vagina, -ae, f.: sheath, vagina
durus, -a, -um, adj.: hard
rego, pp. rectus, v.: to straighten, guide, direct
truncus, -i, m.: stem, trunk

nucleus, -i, m.: kernel or inside of anything
scrotum, -i, n.: bag, scrotum
regio, -onis, f.: territory, region
testis, -is, m.: testicle
mors, mortis, f.: death
tarsus, -i, m.: instep
rana, -ae, f.: frog
medulla, -ae, f.: marrow
uterus, -i, m.: womb
penis, -is, m.: male organ of copulation
collum, -i, n.: neck

88. Define etymologically:

postuterine
noctambulation
penile
carboniferous
mortal
medullar
vaginal
tarsotibial
dural
uterocervical
subnormal
vaginolabial
ramose
mortality
tibiofibular
circumscribe
pilar
ramification
interdental
vesicovaginal
tussicular
conclusion
productivity
toleration
lenitive
petrify

supramaxillary
medullary
plumose
ranine
tussive
regional
arboriform
unguinal
palatiform
antitussive
medullispinal
pilose
utero-ovarian
uterosacral
truncal
conversion
vesiculiform
ventrose
manuscript
abdomino-anterior
intrascrotal
solution
verbosity
juncture
quantity
commissural

incertitude
concoctor
vertebromammary
incisor
ramal
pontile
ramulose
subvertebral
uterine
palatonasal
pontine
mortiferous
ramiform
incisure
ranarium
cloacal
reflection
vaginoabdominal
post-tussis
ramify
nerviduct
reticular
incurability
mellifluous
falciform
clavicle

Notes:

LESSON XI

89. Translate and give the exact scientific definition of each of the following words or groups of words:

1. cornu majus
2. nucleus cerebelli
3. medulla spinalis
4. collum humeri
5. vagina pili
6. mento-anterior
7. funiculus medullae spinalis
8. membrana abdominis

90. Translate the following medical terms:

1. caput et humerus
2. palpebra superior
3. dorsum nasi
4. labium inferius
5. vertebrae verae
6. os breve
7. cavum abdominis
8. digiti manus
9. facies lateralis
10. musculi capitis
11. musculus longus colli
12. truncus intestinalis
13. radix pulmonis
14. collum femoris

91. Memorize the following expressions, abbreviations, and meanings sometimes found in prescriptions:

Term or Phrase	*Abbreviation*	*Meaning*
bibe	bib.	drink
in vitro	in vit.	in glass
illico	illic.	immediately
cyathus	cyath.	a glassful
aqua destillata	aq. dest.	distilled water
durante dolore	dur. dol.	while the pain lasts
sinapis	sinap.	mustard
dimidius	dim.	one-half
in loco fervente	in loc. ferv.	in a hot place
in loco frigido	in loc. frig.	in a cold place
recipe	℞	take

92. Give the locations of the following regions of the body's surface:

1. regio frontalis
2. regio dorsalis manus
3. regio coxae
4. regio colli lateralis
5. regio colli anterior
6. regio mammalis
7. regio abdominis lateralis
8. regio lumbalis
9. regio sacralis
10. regio femoris lateralis
11. regio dorsalis pedis
12. genu posterior
13. regio mentalis
14. regio nasalis

Notes:

LESSON XII

93. Vocabulary

jaculum, -i, n.: dart
adeps, adipis, m. or f.: fat
plica, -ae, f.: fold, plait
axilla, -ae, f.: armpit
fetus, -us, m.: offspring
bilis, -is, f.: bile
folium, -i, n.: leaf
uncus, -i, m.: hook
tubus, -i, m.: pipe, tube
spatium, -i, n.: space, room, interval
vivus, -a, -um, adj.: living, alive
squama, -ae, f.: scale

jecur, -oris, n.: liver
plexus, -us, m.: braid, plaiting
jugulum, -i, n.: throat, neck
bulbus, -i, m.: plant bulb
placenta, -ae, f.: flat cake
barba, -ae, f.: beard
seco, pp. sectus, v.: to cut
vulva, -ae, f.: womb
tuber, -eris, n.: swelling
intestinum, -i, n.: intestines, guts, bowels
stratum, -i, n.: covering
vomer, -eris, m.: ploughshare

94. Define etymologically:

bulbiform
bisect
tubercle
vivisection
contraindicant
malediction
foliose
jaculiferous
abdominovesical
stratiform
squamosal
jugular
nigritude
adipocellular
vitric
flexible
plexal
lobular
ossiform
resect
inclusion

tubule
bilious
foliar
trident
vulval
squamate
bicaudal
indication
viviparous
jecoral
oviparous
axillary
refrangible
nigrification
apposition
parturient
vivify
fetation
millenary
squamulate
tussive

insection
bilifaction
uterovaginal
trisect
unciform
tubo-ovarian
feticide
quinquetubercular
adiposity
omniform
vivisectorium
bulbopontine
vulvovaginal
tuberiferous
plexiform
ramify
intersection
stratification
benediction
proximolingual
unilaminar

95. State the etymological and scientific definition of each of the following words:

1. flexor
4. vomer
7. vaginate

2. iliospinal
5. fetal
8. palate

3. intravesical
6. plica
9. incisura

Notes:

LESSON XII

96. Translate the following Latin terms and phrases:

1. squama occipitalis
2. stratum corneum
3. regiones pectoris
4. funiculus lateralis
5. plexus dentalis superior
6. plica interdigitalis
7. plicae adiposae
8. bulbus pili
9. bulbus cordis
10. folia linguae
11. jecur adiposum
12. regiones corporis
13. rami ventrales
14. musculi colli
15. corpus tibiae
16. stratum spinosum

97. Explain the following medical terms or phrases:

1. multiple fetation
2. axillary space
3. placenta
4. vaccine
5. inguinal plexus
6. puerperal period
7. vagina cordis
8. filiform pulse
9. pontile
10. gingival

98. Supply the nominative plural form and the meaning of each of these Latin words:

1. fascis
2. radix
3. dens
4. arbor
5. filum
6. bacillus
7. acetum
8. guttur
9. vena
10. furca
11. nervus
12. dolor
13. dies
14. infans
15. pectus

99. Give the Latin term and the English meaning of each of these abbreviations:

1. o.n.
2. ut dict.
3. s.o.s.
4. aa.
5. suppos.
6. gtt.
7. tab.
8. cap.
9. M.
10. q.i.d.
11. C.
12. d.t.d.
13. non rep.
14. p.r.n.
15. h.s.

100. Supply the gender of each of the following Latin nouns:

1. vomer
2. jecur
3. plexus
4. vulva
5. pons
6. tuber
7. guttur
8. viscus
9. tussis
10. vacca
11. squama
12. regio
13. fovea
14. jaculum
15. mus

Notes:

LESSON XIII

101. Vocabulary

navis, -is, *f.*: ship
pello, *pp.* pulsus, v.: to beat, drive
pulsus, -us, *m.*: beating, stroke
pollex, -icis, *m.*: thumb
penna, -ae, *f.*: feather
muto, *pp.* -atus, v.: to change
fortis, -e, adj.: strong
mucus, -i, *m.*: mucous matter of the nose
pius, -a, -um, adj.: pious, gentle, tender
scutum, -i, *n.*: shield
hamus, -i, *m.*: hook
regula, -ae, *f.*: rule, stick
odor, -oris, *m.*: scent, smell, odor

musca, -ae, *f.*: fly
mater, matris, *f.*: mother
nodus, -i, *m.*: knot
nevus, -i, *m.*: birthmark
vacuus, -a, -um, adj.: empty
hallux, -ucis, *m.*: great toe
nebula, -ae, *f.*: cloud, fog, mist
tardus, -a, -um, adj.: slow
naris, -is, *f.*: nostril
semen, -inis, *n.*: seed
nutrio, *pp.* nutritus, v.: to feed, nourish
punctum, -i, *n.*: point, prick
rigidus, -a, -um, adj.: stiff, unbending, rigid

102. Define etymologically:

regularity
nevose
mortify
puncture
mucous
manufacture
scutiform
mutation
omnific
longirostral
scutate
hamular
muciferous
omnipotency
fortitude
nodulous
compeller
supernutrition
nigrify
compressure
rejector
postmortal
ossifluent

subjectivity
pulse
odorous
nodal
punctate
seminal
repellance
muscicide
pennate
vivisector
vertebrosacral
seminiferous
nodose
monition
hallucal
impel
narial
vivification
sternad
sacro-anterior
increase
delactation
imperforation

pulsate
nutrient
nasal
ramisection
odoriferous
fortify
piety
punctiform
sinistrocular
compel
nebular
matricide
tubiform
septilateral
punctual
semipenniform
muciform
rigidity
postnodular
expressional
divisor
insemination
component

Notes:

LESSON XIII

103. Translate the following medical terms:

1. os costale
2. os coxae
3. hallux rigidus
4. pulsus tardus
5. punctum proximum
6. anterior naris
7. fibra nasi
8. nodus cerebri
9. pulsus abdominalis
10. nevus pilosus
11. os intermaxillare
12. pia mater
13. pollex pedis
14. scutum pectoris

104. Give the etymological and scientific meaning of each of these terms:

1. navicular
2. pennate muscle
3. genupectoral position
4. omnivorous
5. guttural pulse
6. maternity hospital

105. List two or more English words derived from each of the following Latin words:

1. **dignus, -a, -um,** adj.: worthy
2. **pediculus, -i,** *m.:* louse
3. **nidus, -i,** *m.:* nest
4. **frux, frugis,** *f.:* fruit
5. **caelebs, -libis,** adj.: unmarried, single
6. **nascor,** *pp.* **natus,** v.: to be born

106. Identify the following parts of the body:

1. scapula	2. costa	3. manus	4. carpus
5. humerus	6. ulna	7. cervix	8. dens
9. inguen	10. sacrum	11. cor	12. mamma
13. coxa	14. maxilla	15. guttur	16. talus
17. cerebrum	18. pectus	19. gingiva	20. collum
21. abdomen	22. vagina	23. testis	24. jecur

107. Give the Latin term and English meaning of each of the following abbreviations:

1. R	2. bib.	3. aq. dest.	4. in vit.
5. illic.	6. in loc. ferv.	7. dur. dol.	8. cyath.
9. ex aq.	10. sol.	11. p.c.	12. ft.

Notes:

LESSON XIV

108. Vocabulary

columna, -ae, *f.:* column
magnus, -a, -um, adj.: great, large
mitto, *pp.* **missus,** v.: to send
ostium, -i, *n.:* door, entrance, opening
frenum, -i, *n.:* bridle, reins, bit
fungus, -i, *m.:* mushroom, fungus
mitigo, *pp.*-**atus,** v.: to make soft
sanus, -a, -um, adj.: sound, healthy, sane
flagellum, -i, *n.:* whip
cella, -ae, *f.:* storehouse, room
genero, *pp.* -**atus,** v.: to beget
collis, -is, *m.:* hill
grex, gregis, *m.:* flock, herd

struma, -ae, *f.:* swelling, tumor
stria, -ae, *f.:* channel, ridge, furrow
strio, *pp.* -**atus,** v.: to striate, flute
sebum, -i, *n.:* grease, fat, tallow
uber, -eris, adj.: fertile, fruitful, copious
centrum, -i, *n.:* center, middle point
vulnus, -eris, *n.:* wound
urtica, -ae, *f.:* nettle
mollis, -e, adj.: soft
pleo, *pp.* **pletus,** v.: to fill
macula, -ae, *f.:* spot

109. Define etymologically:

irregularity	posttibial	commuter
columnar	cell	mitigate
magnify	visibility	bulbiferous
fungiform	remit	striate
generative	mollify	central
uberous	insane	bicaudate
vulnerable	centrilobular	flagellate
permission	implement	generation
strumiform	magnifiable	sanity
septemvir	urtication	decentration
plumosity	degeneration	segregation
magnitude	ulcerative	cellular
remitter	macular	mollifiable
depletion	ostial	cellulicidal
preparative	sanatorium	stricellular
mitigator	adipic	uberty
maculation	vulnerary	frenal
flagellation	columniation	internode
immaculate	mollifier	intermittence
callisection	magnifical	maculopapule
permutation	sanitation	centrad
complementary	urticant	fortification
intromit	matricidal	longipedate
prolabium	subparietal	transection
emiter	transduction	superconductive

Notes:

LESSON XIV

110. Translate and give the medical definition of each of the following:

1. struma mollis
2. cella media
3. frenum linguae
4. colliculus
5. rami dorsales
6. frenulum
7. ostium abdominale tubae uterinae
8. columnella
9. pulsus magnus
10. tarsus inferior
11. ligamentum palpebrale externum
12. pediculus capitis
13. substantia vitrea
14. vertebra magna
15. ligamentum collaterale tibiale
16. corpus adiposum buccae

111. Write the number of the correct matching word in the second column before its definition in the first column:

..... pertaining to the nails   1. tussicular
..... food   2. aliment
..... terse   3. inguinal
..... having only one opening   4. nigritude
..... relating to a cough   5. concise
..... sense of taste   6. unguinal
..... a splitting   7. acetic
..... pertaining to the groin   8. gustation
..... sour   9. uniforate
..... blackness   10. scission

112. Match the columns by placing the correct numbers in the second column before each Latin abbreviation in the first column:

..... o.n.   1. while the pain lasts
..... in vit.   2. in a hot place
..... dur. dol.   3. mixture
..... in loc.ferv.   4. from day to day
..... mist.   5. do not repeat
..... ut dict.   6. in glass
..... g.i.d.   7. water
..... non rep.   8. four times a day
..... aq.   9. every night
..... de d. in di.   10. as directed

Notes:

LESSON XV

113. Vocabulary

erro, *pp.* -atus, v.: to err, wander
cortex, -icis, *m.:* bark, outer layer
trochlea, -ae, *f.:* pulley
putris, -e, adj.: rotten
germen, -inis, *n.:* sprout, bud, germ
septum, -i, *n.:* partition, enclosure
crus, cruris, *n.:* leg
ensis, -is, *m.:* sword
moles, -is, *f.:* mass
sopor, -oris, *m.:* deep sleep
angina, -ae, *f.:* quinsy
soror, -oris, *f.:* sister
flamma, -ae, *f.:* flame

ferrum, -i, *n.:* iron
rado, *pp.* rasus, v.: to scrape, rub
cartilago, -inis, *f.:* gristle, cartilage
lympha, -ae, *f.:* clear spring water
halo, *pp.* -atus, v.: to breathe
fimbria, -ae, *f.:* fringe, border
occulo, *pp.* occultus, v.: to hide, cover
canis, -is, *m.* or *f.:* dog
felis, -is, *f.:* cat
sterilis, -e, adj.: barren, not fertile, sterile
gibbus, -i, *m.:* hump
palpo, *pp.* -atus, v.: to touch gently

114. Define etymologically:

intercrural
cortical
errant
germ
sororicide
putrefy
permissibility
lymphaceus
erratic
inflammability
fimbriate
cartilaginous
petrify
ferric
crural
corticifugal
exhale
putrid
ensiform
abrasion
palpable
fungicidal
commutation
transcortical

exhalation
inhale
visual
signification
stratify
nodular
occult
longitude
pediculous
putrefaction
magnific
gibbous
canine
sorority
corticate
lymphoduct
inflammation
gibbosity
germinal
intermission
vertebrocostal
vesicouterovaginal
mortification
inversion

rehalation
inflammable
cartilage
ensiferous
intestinal
sterility
palpation
inhaler
molecular
insanity
germicidal
soporific
feline
abrade
inhalation
aberrant
ferriferous
cartilaginification
anginal
mutable
intra-abdominal
mitigable
felicity
secundiparity

Notes:

LESSON XV

115. Translate the following medical expressions:

1. septum linguae
2. trochlea humeri
3. nodus cordis
4. angina pectoris
5. crus longum
6. cartilago gutturalis
7. dorsum nasi
8. musculi colli
9. os magnum
10. columna adiposa
11. trochlea femoris
12. crus breve
13. digiti manus
14. regiones corporis
14. labium inferius
16. ostium abdominale
17. angina abdominis
18. ligamentum colli costae
19. septum musculare ventriculorum
20. vena cordis magna

116. Translate and provide the medical definition of each of the following Latin terms:

1. septum
2. lympha
3. scutum
4. trochlea
5. regio lumbalis
6. squama temporalis
7. facies lateralis
8. stratum fibrosum
9. gyrus frontalis superior
10. rami ventrales
11. os breve
12. nodus gutturis

117. Prepare a list of 35 words derived from Latin which would be of use to a student of anatomy. Consult a medical dictionary in order to determine the scientific and etymological meaning of each word on your list.

118. Supply the meaning and the past participle of each Latin verb:

1. divido
2. rego
3. mitto
4. rado
5. pello
6. findo
7. seco
8. caedo

119. Give the abbreviation and the meaning of each of these Latin terms which are sometimes found in prescriptions:

1. aqua
2. illico
3. pilulae
4. pone
5. adde
6. ut dictum
7. trochisci
8. misce
9. doses
10. capsula
11. ante cibos
12. signa

120. List the Latin rules for a long syllable, give an example of each rule, and state the rule for accent.

Notes:

LESSON XVI

121. Vocabulary

vita, -ae, f.: life
duro, pp. -atus, v.: to harden
cedo, pp. cessus, v.: to go
pituita, -ae, f.: phlegm, rheum
corona, -ae, f.: crown
planto, pp. -atus, v.: to plant
gradior, pp. gressus, v.: to step, walk
tango, pp. tactus, v.: to touch
immunis, -e, adj.: free from service
glans, glandis, f.: acorn
fugo, pp. -atus, v.: to put to flight
sinus, -us, m.: a fold, cavity
puber, -eris, f.: an adult
fungor, pp. functus, v.: to perform, serve
pilo, pp. -atus, v.: to plunder, heap together

heres, heredis, c.: an heir
calx, calcis, f.: limestone
pendeo, pp. pensus, v.: to hang down
spargo, pp. sparsus, v.: to scatter
granum,-i, n.: a grain, seed
calor, -oris, m.: heat
lux, lucis, f.: light
vertex, -icis, m.: whirl
puto, pp. -atus, v.: to reckon, calculate
persona, -ae, f.: mask
orbis, -is, m.: a circle
pubes, -is, f.: hair on genitals, genitals
cuspis, -idis, f.: a point
vermis, -is, m.: worm, grub
curro, pp. cursus, v.: to run

122. Define etymologically:

implant	impletion	oviduct
pituitary	propulsion	calcification
cuspad	infrasonic	precostal
calciferous	lucifugal	infrascapular
vermicidal	dispersive	immunodepressant
reactor	conductance	irradiation
computer	extraction	coronary
particulate	pubovesical	verticomental
induction	cuspidate	heredoimmunity
immunodeficiency	transplant	granule
puberty	processor	orbicular
intervention	compiler	glandule
impalpable	semiconductor	replant
postcubital	transfection	personality
apperception	occlusion	infusible
invagination	interplant	extramural
convection	induration	contralateral
vermiform	malfunction	subgemmal
genucubital	calory	vertical
postnatal	introflection	claviform
calorifacient	implantation	heredity
inclusion	dispersion	vermiculous
retrograde	contact	vital

123. Provide the Latin abbreviation for each of the following terms sometimes used in prescriptions:

1. daily
2. a dose
3. in glass
4. at bedtime
5. before meals
6. twice daily
7. write
8. mix

Notes:

LESSON XVI

124. Memorize the following expressions, abbreviations, and meanings sometimes found in prescriptions:

Term or Phrase	Abbreviation	Meaning
charta cerata	chart. cerat.	waxed paper
cochleare amplum	coch. amp.	tablespoonful
cochleare infans	coch. inf.	teaspoonful
syrupus	syr.	syrup
talis; tales; talia	tal.	such
pro usu externo	pro us. ext.	for external use
phiala prius agitata	p.p.a.	the bottle first being shaken
in vaso clauso	in vas. claus.	in a closed vessel
quantitatem sufficientem	q.s.	a sufficient quantity
pulvis; pulveres	pulv.	powder; powders
utendus	utend.	to be used

125. Translate and give the medical definition of each of the following:

1. palpebra inferior
2. labium superius
3. mons pubis
4. corona dentis
5. corona capitis
6. cuspis coronae
7. cuspis dentis
8. venae cerebri internae

126. Identify the following parts of the body:

1. auris
2. facies
3. oculis
4. nasus
5. cervix
6. truncus
7. pelvis
8. crus
9. pes
10. femur
11. sternum
12. tibia
13. fibula
14. frons
15. dorsum
16. labium
17. lingua
18. bucca
19. mentum
20. scapula

127. Translate:

1. Recipe unciam aquae. Misce syrupum.
2. Mitte capsulas decem.
3. Sig.: Utend. ut dict. pro us. ext.
4. M. in vas. claus. Sig.: Cap. unciam sin. aq. b.i.d.
5. M. et mitte tales doses numero L in charta cerata.
6. M. Ft. tab. xix. Sig.: Duo ex aq. o.m. dur. dol.
7. Capiat guttas sex post cibos.
8. Capiat unam pilulam et cochleare infans syrupi omni die.
9. M. Ft. dos. tal. no. xxiv. Disp. in charta cerat. Sig.: ut dict.
10. Div. in cap. no. xx. Sig.: Duo cum aqua p.c. et h.s.

Notes:

Notes:

LESSON XVII

GENERAL REVIEW

128. Indicate the meaning of each of the following prefixes and suffixes:

1. -lent	2. semi- ....
3. circum-	4. dif- ....
5. -ine	6. post- ....
7. -ad	8. oc- ....
9. prae-	10. -ory ....
11. sub-	12. re- ....
13. -ate	14. se- ....
15. juxta-	16. -an ....

129. Supply the meanings of the following Latin words:

1. nebula	2. foramen ....
3. tuber	4. lympha ....
5. voro	6. conus ....
7. emulgeo	8. bene ....
9. oleum	10. adeps ....

130. Supply the genitive ending and the meaning of each of these Latin nouns:

1. vomer	2. tempus ....
3. scutum	4. pulmo ....
5. luna	6. viscus ....
7. sensus	8. lupus ....
9. naris........	10. facies ....

131. List three derivatives for each of the following Latin words:

1. omnis ....
2. facio ....
3. flo ....
4. forma ....
5. premo ....
6. loco ....
7. capio ....
8. moveo ....
9. lingua ....
10. oculus ....

132. Supply the meaning and the past participle of each of the following Latin verbs:

1. flecto...
2. pello...

GENERAL REVIEW

  3. **moneo**..
  4. **spicio** ....
  5. **signo**...
  6. **misceo** ....
  7. **premo**..
  8. **audio** ....
  9. **frango**...
10. **divido**...

133. State the combining forms of the following Latin nouns:

1. **semen**	2. **bacca** ....
3. **facies**	4. **odor** ....
5. **mors**	6. **callus** ....
7. **sensus**	8. **cancer** ....
9. **femur**	10. **lignum** ....

134. Define etymologically:

  1. postpalatine   ....
        ....
  2. preinduction   ....
        ....
  3. reference   ....
        ....
  4. retrocollic   ....
        ....
  5. superalimentation ....
        ....
  6. dentilabial   ....
        ....
  7. visceroparietal   ....
        ....
  8. parturifacient   ....
        ....
  9. vasoformative   ....
        ....
10. ramification   ....
        ....
11. setiform   ....
        ....
12. sanguifacient   ....
        ....
13. subnormality   ....
        ....
14. scapulohumeral   ....
        ....

GENERAL REVIEW

15. nervimotility ....
....
16. regeneration ....
....
17. computation ....
....
18. hepatalgia ....
....
19. toleration ....
....
20. incurable ....
....

135. Match the columns by placing the correct number in the second column before each abbreviation in the first column:

..... o.d.   1. drops
..... sinap.   2. do not repeat
..... s.o.s.   3. daily
..... gtt.   4. mustard
..... M.   5. plaster
..... b.i.d.   6. mix
..... emp.   7. in glass
..... in vit.   8. if necessary
..... non rep.   9. twice a day
..... p.r.n.   10. as the occasion arises

136. Give the Latin term and English meaning of each of the following abbreviations:

1. in loc. ferv. ....
2. O. ....
3. ft. ....
4. dur. dol. ....
5. lin. ....
6. abs. feb. ....
7. Sig. ....
8. h.s. ....
9. d.t.d. ....
10. pil. ....
11. q.s. ....
12. no. ....
13. sin. aq. ....
14. p.p.a. ....
15. cap. ....

GENERAL REVIEW

137. Translate:

1. partes corporis: caput, collum et genu ....
   ....
2. arbor vitae ....
3. penna nasi..
4. ramus nasalis superior ....
5. sulcus occipitotemporalis ....
6. pars media lobuli parietalis inferioris..........................
   ....
7. os uteri externum ....
8. nervi dentales superiores posteriores..........................
   ....
9. vena intercostalis superior sinistra ....
   ....
10. ligamentum mediale carpi ....
11. regio femoris lateralis.......................................
12. musculus longissimus dorsi ....
13. regio suprascapularis ....
14. angina pectoris ....
15. venae intercostales posteriores ....
    ....
16. ligamentum capitis femoris....................................
17. musculus interspinalis cervicis...............................
18. plica interdigitalis ....
19. musculus pectoralis major ....
20. pediculosis corporis..

138. Translate:

1. M. Ft. syr. Sig.: ℥ iii t.i.d.
2. M. Ft. lin. pro us. ext. p.r.n., p.p.a.
3. Div. mass in pil. xii.
4. M. in vas. claus. q.s. sin aq.
5. Add. pulverem in cyatho aquae et cap. omni die si opus sit.

139. Below the following groups of eight definitions are ten terms, only eight of which are correct for the eight definitions given. Place the number of each of the correct terms before the definition to which it belongs.

Group I

..... resembling the brain in struc-   ..... feeding on herbs
       ture
..... surrounding a bud-like body   ..... pertaining to the head and
                              feet

GENERAL REVIEW

..... having the shape of a heart
..... the process of decaying

..... affecting only one side
..... abnormal

1. cordiform
2. putrefaction
3. aberrant
4. unilateral
5. cerebriform
6. capitopedal
7. herbivorous
8. manuduction
9. circumgemmal
10. postbrachial

Group II

..... pertaining to a dog
..... left-footed
..... near the kidney
..... pertaining to the neck

..... toward the tail
..... left-handedness
..... near a nerve
..... pertaining to the loin and
flank

1. adrenal
2. cervical
3. sinistrality
4. canine
5. caudad
6. sinistropedal
7. adnerval
8. manual
9. iliolumbar
10. dextropedal

Group III

..... under the ear
..... egg-shaped
..... pertaining to the nose and
mouth
..... a sleep producing drug

..... the upper jaw bone
..... conducting blood
..... joining or flowing together
..... an investigative dissection on
a living animal

1. confluent
2. sanguiferous
3. subaural
4. oronasal
5. oviform
6. vivisection
7. somniferous
8. postdural
9. supramaxilla
10. somnifacient

Bibliography

AGARD, WALTER R., AND H. M. HOWE. *Medical Greek and Latin at a Glance* (3rd ed.). New York: Paul B. Hoeber, 1955.

BAILEY, L.H. *How Plants Get Their Names.* New York: The Macmillan Company, 1933.

Blakiston's New Gould Medical Dictionary (2nd ed.). New York: McGraw-Hill Book Company, 1956.

BORROR, DONALD J. *Dictionary of Word Roots and Combining Forms.* Palo Alto: N-P Publications, 1960.

BROWN, CHARLES B. *The Contribution of Greek to English.* Nashville: Vanderbilt University Press, 1942.

BROWN, RONALD W. *Composition of Scientific Words.* Washington, D.C.: Published by the Author, 1956.

CLARK, WALLACE, AND ANN CLARK. *Guide to Medical Terminology.* Philadelphia: F.A. Davis Company, 1959.

BURRISS, ELI E., AND LIONELL CASSON. *Latin and Greek in Current Use.* New York: Prentice-Hall, 1948.

COLLINS, JOSEPH V. *English Words of Latin and Greek Origin.* Stevens Point: Worzalla Publishing Company, 1939.

DORFMAN, JACOB S. *Pharmaceutical Latin.* Philadelphia: Lea & Febiger, 1938.

Dorland's Illustrated Medical Dictionary (23rd ed.). Philadelphia: W. B. Saunders Company, 1959.

Dorland's Illustrated Medical Dictionary (26th ed.). Philadelphia: W. B. Saunders Company, 1981.

HENDERSON, I. F., AND W. D. HENDERSON. *A Dictionary of Scientific Terms* (7th ed. revised by J. H. Kenneth). New York: D. Van Nostrand Company, 1960.

HOUGH, JOHN N. *Scientific Terminology.* New York: Rinehart and Company, 1953.

JACKSON, BENJAMIN D. *A Glossary of Botanic Terms* (4th ed.). New York: Hafner Publishing Company, 1950.

JOHNSON, EDWIN L. *Latin Words of Common English.* Boston: D.C. Heath and Company, 1931.

HOCKING, GEORGE M. *A Dictionary of Terms in Pharmacognosy.* Springfield: Thomas, 1955.

JAEGER, EDMUND C. *A Source-Book of Biological Names and Terms* (2nd ed.). Springfield: Thomas, 1950.

_____.*A Source-Book of Medical Terms.* Springfield: Thomas, 1953.

LEWIS, CAROLYN. *Medical Latin.* Francestown: Marshall Jones Company, 1948.

LEWIS, CHARLTON T., AND CHARLES SHORT. *A Latin Dictionary.* Oxford: The Clarendon Press, 1958.

LIDDELL, H. G., AND ROBERT SCOTT. *Greek-English Lexicon* (9th ed.). Oxford: The Clarendon Press, 1940.

The Macmillan Medical Dictionary. New York: The Macmillan Company, 1957.

MULDOON, HUGH C. *Lessons in Pharmaceutical Latin and Prescription Writing and Interpretation* (4th ed.). New York: John Wiley & Sons, 1955.

NYBAKKEN, OSCAR E. *Greek and Latin in Scientific Terminology.* Ames: Iowa State College Press, 1959.

PEPPER, O. H. PERRY. *Medical Etymology.* Philadelphia: W. B. Saunders Company, 1954.

SKEAT, WALTER W. *A Concise Etymological Dictionary of the English Language.* Oxford: The Clarendon Press, 1901.

SKINNER, HENRY A. *The Origin of Medical Terms.* Baltimore: Williams and Wilkins Company, 1949.

SOUTER, A. *A Glossary of Later Latin to 600 A.D.* Oxford: The Clarendon Press, 1949.

Stedman's Medical Dictionary (19th ed.). Baltimore: Williams and Wilkins, 1957.

Stedman's Medical Dictionary (24th ed.). Baltimore: Williams and Wilkins, 1982.

STEINMETZ, E.F. *Codex Vegetabilis* (2nd ed.). Amsterdam: E.F. Steinmetz, 1957.

Webster's Third New International Dictionary (Unabridged). Springfield: G. & C. Merriam Company, 1961.

WOODS, ROBERT S. *The Naturalist's Lexicon.* Pasadena: Abbey Garden Press, 1944.

GREEK-ENGLISH VOCABULARY

Roman numerals indicate the chapter in which a word was first introduced.

A

aden, adenos, n.: gland XII

aēr, aēros, n.: air XIII

aisthesis, -eos, n.: sensation, perception V

akouo, v.: to hear X

akron, n.: point, extremity, summit V

aktis, aktinos, n.: ray IX

algos, n.: pain I

allos, adj.: other VI

allotrios, adj.: foreign, strange XIV

amblys, adj.: dull VI

amphoteros, adj.: both IV

amylon, n.: starch XV

aner, andros, n.: man, male XI

angeion, n.: vessel I

ankyle, n.: stiff joint XV

ankyra, n.: anchor, hook X

anthropos, n.: man X

apotheke, n.: storehouse III

arachne, n.: spider VI

arche, n.: beginning, origin VII

archos, n.: rectum XV

argyros, n.: silver XIV

arithmos, n.: number II

arteria, n.: windpipe, artery II

arthron, n.: joint II

aster, asteros, n.: star II

asthma, -atos, n.: hard-drawn breath X

astron, n.: constellation, star II

ateles, adj.: imperfect, incomplete III

atmos, n.: vapor, steam VI

autos, pron.: self XV

B

bakterion, n.: rod, staff XV

ballo, v.: to throw VI

bapto, v.: to dip, dye XIV

baros, n.: weight, pressure IX

basis, -eos, n.: foundation, step III

bathys, adj.: deep V

bios, n.: life I

blastos, n.: germ, sprout IV

blennos, n.: mucus V

blepharon, n.: eyelid IX

bole, n.: throw VI

boule, n.: will XIII

bous, n.: ox XIII

boutyron, n.: butter XIII

brachion, n.: arm XIII

brachys, adj.: short VII

bradys, adj.: slow V

broma, -atos, n.: food III

bronchos, n.: windpipe XIII

C

cheilos, n.: lip XI

cheir, cheiros, n.: hand I

chloros, adj.: green XV

chole, n.: bile V

chondros, n.: cartilage IX

chorde, n.: cord XV

chorion, n.: skin III

chroma, -atos, n.: color IV

chronos, n.: time IX

159

D

daktylos, n.: finger XI

delos, adj.: evident, clear XII

delphys, delphyos, n.: uterus XIII

demos, n.: people XI

dendron, n.: tree VII

dere, n.: neck XIV

derma, -atos, n.: skin IV

desmos, n.: ligament, fetter XIV

deuteros, adj.: second XIV

didymos, n.: twin (testicles) XIII

dis, adv.: twice, double XIII

dromos, n.: running VI

dynamis, -eos, *and* -ios, n.: power, force III

E

echo, echoos, n.: echo XII

ektasis, -eos, n.: expansion, extension, stretching III

ektrosis, -eos, n.: miscarriage XV

elaion, n.: oil XII

elektron, n.: amber IX

emesis, -eos, n.: vomiting XIII

enantios, adj.: opposite, face-to-face VII

enchyma, atos, n.: infusion, juice IX

enkephalos, n.: brain IV

enteron, n.: intestine, bowel V

eos, n.: dawn XIV

ergon, n.: work, energy X

eros, erotos, n.: love XII

erythros, adj.: red II

G

gala, galaktos, n.: milk II

gamete, n.: wife VII

gametes, n.: spouse VII

gamos, n.: marriage I

gaster (gastr-), gasteros, n.: stomach IX

ge, n.: earth II

genesis, -eos, n.: origin, descent, generation, production II

geron, gerontos, n.: old man XI

gignomai (gen(e)-, gon-), v.: become, beget, produce II

glossa, n.: tongue IV

glykys, adj.: sweet; the combining form *glyco-* usually denotes sugar III

gnathos, n.: jaw VII

gnosis, -eos, n.: knowledge VII

gramma, n.: a drawing IX

grapho, v.: to write I

gymnos, adj.: naked XII

gyne, gynaikos, n.: woman X

H

haima, -atos, n.: blood II

hals, halos, n.: salt XIV

hapto, v.: to touch XV

hebe, n.: youth XIV

hekaton, num.: hundred XI

helios, n.: sun IV

helix, -ikos, n.: coil XIV

helkos, n.: ulcer XIV

helmin, helminthos, n.: worm XI

hen, henos, num.: one XI

hepar, hepatos, n.: liver XI

hepta, num,: seven XI

heteros, adj.: other, different II

hex, num.: six XI

hexis, -eos, n.: habit IX

hidros, n.: sweat XII

hieros, adj.: holy II

hippos, n.: horse XIV

histos, n.: tissue XII

holos, adj.: whole, entire XV

homos, adj.: same, similar II

hormao (hormon), v.: to excite III

hyalos, n.: glass XII

hydor (hydr-), hydatos, n.: water X

hygros, adj.: moist XII

hymen, hymenos, n.: membrane XI

hystera, n.: uterus IX

I

iatreia, n.: medical treatment V

ichor, ichoros, n.: serum, discharge

XII

ichthys, ichthyos, n.: fish XI
is, inos, n.: fiber, muscle III
isos, adj.: equal I
ixys, ixyos, n.: waist XIII

K

kainos, adj.: new XIII
kakos, adj.: bad IX
kardia, n.: heart IV
karkinoma, -atos, n.: cancer XIII
karpos, n.: wrist XIV
kauter, -eros, n.: branding iron XIII
keimai, v.: to lie down III
kele, n.: tumor, rupture, XII
kephale, n.: head IV
kineo, v.: to move V
kinesis, -eos, n.: movement, motion V
klastos, adj.: broken IX
klon, n.: twig, shoot XV
klonos, n.: turmoil IV
klysis, -eos, n.: injection V
koilia, n.: belly IX
koleos, n.: sheath (vagina) IX
kolla, n.: glue VI
kolon, n.: large intestine, colon V
kolpos, n.: bosom (vagina) III
konis, konios, n.: dust XIII
kopros, n.: dung, feces IX
kranion, n.: skull I
kreas, kreos, n.: flesh XII
krisis, -eos, n.: crisis IV
kryos, adj.: cold XV
kryptos, adj.: hidden II
kteis, ktenos, n.: comb XIV
kyanos, n.: dark blue substance XV
kylindros, n.: roll XIV
kyo, v.: to conceive, be pregnant VII
kyon, kynikos, n.: dog XIII
kystis, -eos *and* **-ios,** n.: bladder IV
kytos, n.: cell II

L

labros, adj.: greedy XII
laleo, v.: to speak XIII

lapara, n.: flank, loin III
larynx, laryngos, n.: larynx V
leios, adj.: smooth XII
lepis, lepidos, n.: scale XII
lepsis, -eos, n.: seizure IX
leukos, adj.: white IV
lexis, -eos, n.: word III
limos, n.: hunger XIII
lipos, n.: fat X
lithos, n.: stone I
logos, n.: discourse, science I
lordos, adj.: bent back III
lyo, v.: to loose VII
lysis, -eos, n.: loosening, dissolution VII

M

makros, adj.: large, long XII
mania, n.: madness III
manos, adj.: thin VI
mastos, n.: breast XV
mechane, n.: machine XIII
megas, megalou, adj.: great, large V
melas, melanos, adj.: black VI
melos, n.: limb XIV
meros, -eos, n.: part IV
mesos, adj.: middle I
metra, n.: womb, uterus XII
metron, n.: measure I
mikros, adj.: small VII
miseo, v.: to hate XIII
mnesis, -eos, n.: remembrance, memory VI
monos, adj.: one, alone, single III
moria, n.: folly, V
morphe, n.: form IV
myelos, n.: marrow VII
myia, n.: fly VI
mys, myos, n.: muscle VII
myxa, n.: mucus VII

N

narke, n.: stupor X
nekros, n.: dead body, corpse II
neos, adj.: new II

nephros, n.: kidney I
nepios, n.: infant XII
neuron, n.: nerve I
nomos, n.: law, custom II
nosos, n.: disease II
nous, nou, n.: mind II
nystagmos, n.: nodding, dozing V
nyx, nyktos, n.: night X

O

odous, odontos, n.: tooth V
odyne, n.: pain V
oidema, -atos, n.: swelling VII
oligos, adj.: few, little, small III
omos, n.: shoulder V
omphalos, n.: navel XII
onkos, n.: tumor XII
onyma, -atos, n.: name XIV
ōon , n.: egg XIV
opisthen, adv.: behind V
ops, opos, n.: eye, vision, VI
opsios, adj.: late VI
opsis, -eos, *and* **-ios,** n.: vision VI
orchis, -eos, *and* **-ios,** n.: testicle XI
orexis, -eos, n.: appetite XV
ornis, ornithos, n.: bird III
oros, n.: whey XIV
orrhos, n.: serum XIV
orthos, adj.: straight I
osme, n.: smell XII
osmos, n.: impulsion X
osteon, n.: bone IX
oulon, n.: gum II
ouron, n.: urine III
ous, otos, n.: ear V
oxys, adj.: sharp, sour XIII

P

pachys, adj.: thick V
pais, paidos, n.: child XII
palaios, adj.: old, ancient XIII
parthenos, n.: maiden XI
pas, pantos, adj.: all, complete X
pathos, n.: suffering, disease IV
penes, adj.: poor III

pente, num.: five XI
pepsis, -eos, n.: digestion XI
pepto, v.: to digest XIV
peros, adj.: maimed XIV
phago, v.: to eat VII
phaios, adj.: dark, dusky V
phallos, n.: penis XI
phantasma, -atos, n.: image V
pharmakon, n.: drug, poison III
pharynx, pharyngos, n.: throat XI
phero, v.: to bear, carry IV
phileo, v.: to love X
phleps, phlebos, n.: vein IX
phlogistos, adj.: burnt, on fire IV
phlox, phlogos, n.: flame IV
phobia, n.: fear, fright II
phone, n.: sound, voice, tone II
phoresis, -eos, n.: a carrying in XII
phoros, adj.: bearing XV
phos, photos, n.: light XI
phren, phrenos, n.: mind X
phyle, n.: tribe, class V
phyton, n.: plant II
piesis, -eos, n.: pressure XIII
pithekos, n.: ape XI
plane, n.: wandering XIII
plastos, adj.: formed, molded VI
plethysmos, n.: enlargement, multiplication III
plexis, -eos, n.: stroke III
pneuma, -atos, n.: air, wind, breath X
pneumon, n.: lung X
poikilos, adj.: varied III
polis, -eos, *and* **-ios,** n.: city XIV
polys, adj.: many, much I
porne, n.: prostitute XV
potamos, n.: river XIV
pous, podos, n.: foot I
presbys, adj.: old, pertaining to old age X
proktos, n.: anus, rectum XII
prosopon, n.: face XV
pseudes, adj.: false, spurious I
psora, n.: itch IV

psyche, n.: mind VII
ptosis, -eos, n.: falling XV
pyelos, n.: trough (pelvis) IV
pyknos, adj.: thick VI
pyle, n.: gate XV
pyon, n.: pus XIV

R

rhachis, (rach-), -ios, n.: spine XV
rheo, v.: to flow II
rheos, n.: stream, current, flow II
rhis, rhinos, n.: nose V

S

salpinx, salpingos, n.: tube, trumpet IX
sapros, adj.: putrid, rotten IX
sarx, sarkos, n.: flesh X
schizo, v.: to split, divide X
seismos, n.: shaking, shock XV
sepsis, -eos, n.: decay II
sitos, n.: food VI
skaphe, n.: boat XIV
skelos, n.: leg XIII
skleros, adj.: hard II
skopeo, v.: to look at, view X
skor, skatos, n.: feces, dung XIII
skotos, n.: darkness X
soma, -atos, n.: body VI
sperma, -atos, n.: seed XII
sphaira, n.: sphere, ball VI
sphen, sphenos, n.: wedge VI
sphygmos, n.: pulse VI
sphyzo, v.: to beat, throb XII
splanchnon, n.: viscus, entrail VII
splen, splenos, n.: spleen VI
spodos, n.: ashes II
spondylos, n.: vertebra, spindle VII
sporos, n.: seed XII
stear, steatos, n.: tallow, fat XV
stenos, adj.: narow IX
stenosis, -eos, n.: narrowing IX
stereos, adj.: solid VII
stethos, n.: breast (male or female) X
sthenos, n.: strength II

stigma, -atos, n.: point, mark VII
stoma, -atos, n.: mouth VI
strobile, n.: twist of lint III
syrinx, syringos, n.: tube, pipe VII

T

tachos, n.: speed I
tachys, adj.: swift I
techne, n.: skill X
tele, adv.: far off VII
telos, -eos, n.: end, completion VII
tetra, tetrados, num.: four XI
thalassa, n.: sea XI
thanatos, n.: death XI
theion, n.: sulphur X
theka, n.: box, case XV
thele, n.: nipple IX
thenar, thenaros, n.: palm of the hand III
theos, n.: God XI
therapeia, n.: treatment IV
therion, n.: wild beast XV
therme, n.: heat IV
thesis, -eos, n.: placing, putting VI
thrix, trichos, n.: hair X
thorax, thorakos, n.: chest X
thrombos, n.: clot IX
thymos, n.: spirit, mind XV
tomos, n.: cutting; the suffix *-tome* often indicates the instrument for cutting I
tonos, n.: stretching, tension V
topos, n.: place, region IX
trachelos, n.: throat, neck I
trauma, -atos, n.: wound XI
treis, tria, num.: three XV
tresis, -eos, n.: perforation, boring VII
tricha, adj.: threefold XV
trigonon, n.: triangle XV
trochos, n.: wheel XIV
trope, n.: turning IV
trophe, n.: nourishment VII
trypesis, -eos, n.: piercing X

typhlos, adj.: blind XV
typos, n.: type VII
tyros, n.: cheese XIII

X

xanthos, adj.: yellow VII
xenos, n.: stranger, guest, foreigner

XII

Z

zoe, n.: life XIII
zoon, n.: animal XII
zyme, n.: leaven X

ENGLISH-GREEK VOCABULARY

A

air: aēr, aēros, n.
air (wind, breath): pneuma, -atos, n.
all (complete): pas, pantos, adj.
amber: elektron, n.
anchor (hook): ankyra, n.
animal: zoon, n.
anus (rectum): proktos, n.
ape: pithekos, n.
appetite: orexis, -eos, n.
arm: brachion, n.
ashes: spodos, n.

B

bad: kakos, adj.
bear (carry): phero, v.
bearing: phoros, adj.
beat (throb): sphyzo, v.
become (beget, produce): gignomai
  (gen(e)-, gon-), v.
beginning (origin): arche, n.
behind: opisthen, adv.
belly: koilia, n.
bent back: lordos, adj.
bile: chole, n.
bird: ornis, ornithos, n.
black: melas, melanos, adj.
bladder: kystis, -eos and -ios, n.
blind: typhlos, adj.
blood: haima, -atos, n.
boat: skaphe, n.
body: soma, -atos, n.
bone: osteon, n.
bosom (vagina): kolpos, n.

both: amphoteros, adj.
box (case): theka, n.
brain: enkephalos, n.
branding iron: kauter, -eros, n.
breast: mastos, n.
breast (male or female): stethos, n.
breath, hard-drawn: asthma, -atos, n.
broken: klastos, adj.
burnt (on fire): phlogistos, adj.
butter: boutyron, n.

C

cancer: karkinoma, -atos, n.
carrying in: phoresis, -eos, n.
cartilage: chondros, n.
cell: kytos, n.
cheese: tyros, n.
chest: thorax, thorakos, n.
child: pais, paidos, n.
city: polis, -eos, and -ios, n.
clot: thrombos, n.
coil: helix, -ikos, n.
cold: kryos, adj.
colon (large intestine): kolon, n.
color: chroma, -atos, n.
comb: kteis, ktenos, n.
conceive (be pregnant): kyo, v.
constellation (star): astron, n.
cord: chorde, n.
crisis: krisis, -eos, n.
cutting: tomos, n.

D

dark (dusky): phaios, adj.

darkness: skotos, n.
dawn: eos, n.
dead body (corpse): nekros, n.
death: thanatos, n.
decay: sepsis, -eos, n.
deep: bathys, adj.
digest: pepto, v.
digestion: pepsis, -eos, n.
dip (dye): bapto, v.
discourse (science): logos, n.
disease: nosos, n.
dog: kyon, kynikos, n.
drawing: gramma, n.
drug (poison): pharmakon, n.
dull: amblys, adj.
dung (feces): kopros, n.
dust: konis, konios, n.

E

ear: ous, otos, n.
earth: ge, n.
eat: phago, v.
echo: echo, echoos, n.
egg: oon, n.
end (completion): telos, -eos, n.
enlargement (multiplication): plethysmos, n.
equal: isos, adj.
evident (clear): delos, adj.
excite: hormao (hormon), v.
expansion (extension, stretching): ektasis, -eos, n.
eye (vision): ops, opos, n.
eyelid: blepharon, n.

F

face: prosopon, n.
falling: ptosis, -eos, n.
false (spurious): pseudes, adj.
far off: tele, adv.
fat: lipos, n.
fear (fright): phobia, n.
feces (dung): skor, skatos, n.
few (little, small): oligos, adj.
fiber (muscle): is, inos, n.

finger: daktylos, n.
fish: ichthys, ichthyos, n.
five: pente, num.
flame: phlox, phlogos, n.
flank (loin): lapara, n.
flesh: kreas, kreos, n.
flesh: sarx, sarkos, n.
flow: rheo, v.
fly: myia, n.
folly: moria, n.
food: broma, -atos, n.
food: sitos, n.
foot: pous, podos, n.
foreign (strange): allotrios, adj.
form: morphe, n.
formed (molded): plastos, adj.
foundation (step): basis, -eos, n.
four: tetra, tetrados, num.

G

gate: pyle, n.
germ (sprout): blastos, n.
gland: aden, adenos, n.
glass: hyalos, n.
glue: kolla, n.
God: theos, n.
great (large): megas, megalou, adj.
greedy: labros, adj.
green: chloros, adj.
gum: oulon, n.

H

habit: hexis, -eos, n.
hair: thrix, trichos, n.
hand: cheir, cheiros, n.
hard: skleros, adj.
hate: miseo, v.
head: kephale, n.
hear: akouo, v.
heart: kardia, n.
heat: therme, n.
hidden: kryptos, adj.
holy: hieros, adj.
horse: hippos, n.
hundred: hekaton, num.

hunger: limos, n.

I

image: phantasma, -atos, n.
imperfect (incomplete): ateles, adj.
impulsion: osmos, n.
infant: nepios, n.
infusion (juice): enchyma, -atos, n.
injection: klysis, -eos, n.
intestine (bowel): enteron, n.
itch: psora, n.

J

jaw: gnathos, n.
joint: arthron, n.

K

kidney: nephros, n.
knowledge: gnosis, -eos, n.

L

large (long): makros, adj.
larynx: larynx, laryngos, n.
late: opsios, adj.
law (custom): nomos, n.
leaven: zyme, n.
leg: skelos, n.
lie down: keimai, v.
life: bios, n.
life: zoe, n.
ligament (fetter): desmos, n.
light: phos, photos, n.
limb: melos, n.
lip: cheilos, n.
liver: hepar, hepatos, n.
look at (view): skopeo, v.
loose: lyo, v.
loosening (dissolution): lysis, -eos, n.
love: eros, erotos, n.
love: phileo, v.
lung: pneumon, n.

M

machine: mechane, n.
madness: mania, n.
maiden: parthenos, n.

maimed: peros, adj.
man (male): aner, andros, n.
man: anthropos, n.
man, old: geron, gerontos, n.
many (much): polys, adj.
marriage: gamos, n.
marrow: myelos, n.
measure: metron, n.
membrane: hymen, hymenos, n.
memory (remembrance): mnesis, -eos, n.
middle: mesos, adj.
milk: gala, galaktos, n.
mind: nous, nou, n.
mind: phren, phrenos, n.
mind: psyche, n.
miscarriage: ektrosis, -eos, n.
moist: hygros, adj.
molded (formed): plastos, adj.
mouth: stoma, -atos, n.
move: kineo, v.
movement (motion): kinesis, -eos, n.
mucus: blennos, n.
mucus: myxa, n.
muscle: mys, myos, n.

N

naked: gymnos, adj.
name: onyma, -atos, n.
narrow: stenos, adj.
narrowing: stenosis, -eos, n.
navel: omphalos, n.
neck: dere, n.
nerve: neuron, n.
new: kainos, adj.
new: neos, adj.
night: nyx, nyktos, n.
nipple: thele, n.
nodding (dozing): nystagmos, n.
nose: rhis, rhinos, n.
nourishment: trophe, n.
number: arithmos, n.

O

oil: elaion, n.

old (ancient): palaios, adj.
old (pertaining to old age): presbys, adj.
one: hen, henos, num.
one (alone, single): monos, adj.
opposite (face-to-face): enantios, adj.
origin (descent, generation, production): genesis, -eos, n.
other: allos, adj.
other (different): heteros, adj.
ox: bous, n.

P

pain: algos, n.
pain: odyne, n.
palm of the hand: thenar, thenaros, n.
part: meros, -eos, n.
pelvis (trough): pyelos, n.
penis: phallos, n.
people: demos, n.
perforation (boring): tresis, -eos, n.
piercing: trypesis, -eos, n.
place (region): topos, n.
placing (putting): thesis, -eos, n.
plant: phyton, n.
point (extremity, summit): akron, n.
point (mark): stigma, -atos, n.
poor: penes, adj.
power (force): dynamis, -eos, *and* -ios, n.
pressure: piesis, -eos, n.
prostitute: porne, n.
pulse: sphygmos, n.
pus: pyon, n.
putrid (rotten): sapros, adj.

R

ray: aktis, aktinos, n.
rectum: archos, n.
red: erythros, adj.
river: potamos, n.
rod (staff): bakterion, n.
roll: kylindros, n.
running: dromos, n.

S

salt: hals, halos, n.
same (similar): homos, adj.
scale: lepis, lepidos, n.
sea: thalassa, n.
second: deuteros, adj.
seed: sperma, -atos, n.
seed: sporos, n.
seizure: lepsis, -eos, n.
self: autos, pron.
sensation (perception): aisthesis, -eos, n.
serum (discharge): ichor, ichoros, n.
serum: orrhos, n.
seven: hepta, num.
shaking (shock): seismos, n.
sharp (sour): oxys, adj.
sheath (vagina): koleos, n.
short: brachys, adj.
shoulder: omos, n.
silver: argyros, n.
six: hex, num.
skill: techne, n.
skin: chorion, n.
skin: derma, -atos, n.
skull: kranion, n.
slow: bradys, adj.
small: mikros, adj.
smell: osme, n.
smooth: leios, adj.
solid: stereos, adj.
sound (voice, tone): phone, n.
speak: laleo, v.
speed: tachos, n.
sphere (ball): sphaira, n.
spider: arachne, n.
spine: rhachis (rach-), -ios, n.
spirit (mind): thymos, n.
spleen: splen, splenos, n.
split (divide): schizo, v.
spouse: gametes, n.
star: aster, asteros, n.
starch: amylon, n.
stiff joint: ankyle, n.

stomach: gaster (gastr-), gasteros, n.
stone: lithos, n.
storehouse: apotheke, n.
straight: orthos, adj.
stranger (guest, foreigner): xenos, n.
stream (current, flow): rheos, n.
strength: sthenos, n.
stretching (tension): tonos, n.
stroke: plexis, -eos, n.
stupor: narke, n.
substance, dark blue: kyanos, n.
suffering (disease): pathos, n.
sugar: glyco, comb. form
sulphur: theion, n.
sun: helios, n.
sweat: hidros, n.
sweet: glykys, adj.
swelling: oidema, -atos, n.
swift: tachys, adj.

T

tallow (fat): stear, steatos, n.
testicle: orchis, -eos, *and* -ios, n.
thick: pachys, adj.
thick: pyknos, adj.
thin: manos, adj.
three: treis, tria, num.
threefold: tricha, adj.
throat: pharynx, pharyngos, n.
throat (neck): trachelos, n.
throw: ballo, v.
throw: bole, n.
time: chronos, n.
tissue: histos, n.
tongue: glossa, n.
tooth: odous, odontos, n.
touch: hapto, v.
treatment: therapeia, n.
treatment, medical: iatreia, n.
tree: dendron, n.
triangle: trigonon, n.
tribe (class): phyle, n.
tube (trumpet): salpinx, salpingos, n.
tube (pipe): syrinx, syringos, n.

tumor (rupture): kele, n.
tumor: onkos, n.
turmoil: klonos, n.
turning: trope, n.
twice (double): dis, adv.
twig (shoot): klon, n.
twin (testicles): didymos, n.
twist of lint: strobile, n.
type: typos, n.

U

ulcer: helkos, n.
urine: ouron, n.
uterus: delphys, delphyos, n.
uterus: hystera, n.

V

vapor (steam): atmos, n.
varied: poikilos, adj.
vein: phleps, phlebos, n.
vertebra (spindle): spondylos, n.
vessel: angeion, n.
viscus (entrail): splanchnon, n.
vision: opsis, -eos *and* -ios, n.
vomiting: emesis, -eos, n.

W

waist: ixys, ixyos, n.
wandering: plane, n.
water: hydor (hydr-), hydatos, n.
wedge: sphen, sphenos, n.
weight (pressure): baros, n.
wheel: trochos, n.
whey: oros, n.
white: leukos, adj.
whole (entire): holos, adj.
wife: gamete, n.
wild beast: therion, n.
will: boule, n.
windpipe (artery): arteria, n.
windpipe: bronchos, n.
woman: gyne, gynaikos, n.
womb (uterus): metra, n.
word: lexis, -eos, n.
work (energy): ergon, n.

worm: helmin, helminthos, n.
wound: trauma, -atos, n.
wrist: karpos, n.
write: grapho, v.

Y

yellow: xanthos, adj.
youth: hebe, n.

Greek Prefixes and Suffixes

PREFIXES

Prefix	*Meaning*
a-, an- (before vowels)	without, lack of, negation
amphi-, ampho-	about, around, on both sides
ana-	up, upon, apart, throughout
anti-	against
apo-, ap-, aph-	away, from
cata-	down, under
dia-	through, apart
dys-	bad, faulty, painful
ec-	out of, from
ecto-, ect-	outside
en-, em-	in
endo-, ento-	within
epi-, ep-, eph-	on, upon
eso-	inward, within
eu-	well, good, easy
exo-	outside, without
hemi-	half
hyper-	over, above, beyond, excessive
hypo-, hyp-	below, under, deficient
meta-, met-, meth-	after, beyond, change
para-, par-	beside, near, abnormal
peri-	around, near
pro-	before
pros-	to, before, near
syn-, sym-	together, with

SUFFIXES

Suffix	Meaning
-ac	concerning or pertaining to
-atic	
-etic	
-ic	
-itic	
-tic	
-esis	state, condition, act, quality of
-sis	
-ia	
-y	
-gen	producing
-osis	disease, increase of, state of
-iasis	
-ism	state, condition, belief, doctrine
-ics	art or science of
-ist	agent, one who practices, professes, or is skilled in
-itis	inflammation
-ize	make, do, practice, change
-oid	like, having the shape of
-tery	place of
-oma	tumor

172

LATIN-ENGLISH VOCABULARY

Roman numerals indicate the chapter in which a word was first introduced.

A

abdomen, -inis, *n.*: belly XI
acer, acris, acre, adj.: sharp, pointed, cutting III
acetum, -i, *n.*: vinegar VI
acidus, -a, -um, adj.: sour VI
adeps, adipis, *m.* or *f.*: fat XII
ago, *pp.* **actus,** v.: to do, perform, make VII
albus, -a, -um, adj.: white V
alo, *pp.* **alitus** *or* **altus,** v.: to nourish VII
alveus, -i, *m.*: cavity I
ambulo, *pp.* **-atus,** v.: to walk I
angina, -ae, *f.*: quinsy XV
anterior, -oris, comp. adj.: before (time or place) I
aqua, -ae, *f.*: water II
arbor, -oris, *f.*: tree VIII
argentum, -i, *n.*: silver VII
audio, *pp.* **auditus,** v.: to hear IV
auris, -is, *f.*: ear II
ausculto, *pp.* **-atus,** v.: to listen to IV
axilla, -ae, *f.*: armpit XII

B

bacca, -ae, *f.*: berry VI
bacillus, -i, *m.*: rod VI
barba, -ae, *f.*: beard XII
bene, adv.: well I
bilis, -is, *f.*: bile XII
bini, -ae, -a, adj.: two by two VI
bis (bi-), adv.: twice VII
brevis, -e, adj.: short X

B

bucca, -ae, *f.*: cheek VI
bulbus, -i, *m.*: plant bulb XII
bursa, -ae, *f.*: purse (sac) I

C

caedo (cid), *pp.* **caesus (cis),** v.: to cut, kill, destroy IX
caelebs, -libis, adj.: unmarried, single XIII
callus, -i, *m.*: hard skin VI
calor, -oris, *m.*: heat XVI
calx, calcis, *f.*: limestone XVI
cancer, -cri, *m.*: crab, cancer X
canis, -is, *m.* or *f.*: dog XV
capio (cipi), *pp.* **captus (cept),** v.: to take, seize, V
caput, -itis, *n.*: head II
carbo, -onis, *m.*: coal VI
carpus, -i, *m.*: wrist IV
cartilago, -inis, *f.*: gristle, cartilage XV
cauda, -ae, *f.*: tail III
cavus, -a, -um, adj.: hollow, concave VI
cedo, *pp.* **cessus,** v.: to go XVI
cella, -ae, *f.*: storehouse, room XIV
centrum, -i, *n.*: center, middle point XIV
centum, num.: one hundred VII
cera, -ae, *f.*: wax VI
cerebrum, -i, *n.*: brain IX
certus, -a, -um, adj.: certain, sure IX
cervix, -icis, *f.*: neck IV
cibus, -i, *m.*: food I

173

cilium, -i, *n.*: eyelid VI
circus, -i, *m.*: circle II
claudico, *pp.* -atus, v.: to limp I
clava, -ae, *f.*: club IX
clavis, -is, *f.*: key IX
cloaca, -ae, *f.*: sewer IX
cludo, *pp.*clusus, v.: to close, shut III
collis, -is, *m.*: hill XIV
collum, -i, *n.*: neck XI
colo, *pp.* cultus, v.: to take care of, cultivate IX
columna, -ae, *f.*: column XIV
commissura, -ae, *f.*: seam, joining together I
conus, -i, *m.*: cone III
copia, -ae, *f.*: plenty I
coquo, *pp.* coctus, v.: to boil IX
cor, cordis, *n.*: heart V
corium, -i, *n.*: leather, skin, hide XI
cornu, -us, *n.*: horn I
corona, -ae, *f.*: crown XVI
corpus, -oris, *n.*: body, mass II
cortex, -icis, *m.*: bark, outer layer XV
costa, -ae, *f.*: rib IV
coxa, -ae, *f.*: hip, hip joint V
cresco, *pp.* cretus, v.: to grow VII
crus, cruris, *n.*: leg XV
cubitum, -i, *n.*: elbow II
cubo (cubit), v.: to lie in bed VII
cuneus, -i, *m.*: wedge III
curo, *pp.* -atus, v.: to take care of, see to IV
curro, *pp.* cursus, v.: to run XVI
cuspis, -idis, *f.*: a point XVI
cutis, -is, *f.*: skin III

D

decem, num.: ten VII
decimus, -a, -um, adj.: tenth VII
dens, dentis, *m.*: tooth V
dexter, -tra, -trum, adj.: right II
dico, *pp.* dictus, v.: to speak, say X
dies, -ei, *f.*: day VII
digitus, -i, *m.*: finger, toe I

dignus, -a, -um, adj.: worthy XIII
dispenso, *pp.* -atus, v.: to distribute by weight V
divido, *pp.* divisus, v.: to divide, separate VI
doceo, *pp.* doctus, v.: to teach, instruct IV
dolor, -oris, *m.*: pain X
dorsum, -i, *n.*: back III
duco, *pp.* ductus, v.: to draw, lead III
ductus, -us, *m.*: duct, canal III
dulcis, -e, adj.: sweet II
duo, duae, duo, adj.: two VII
duro, *pp.* -atus, v.: to harden XVI
durus, -a, -um, adj.: hard XI

E

emulgeo, *pp.* emulsus, v.: to drain, milk out I
ensis, -is, *m.*: sword XV
equus, -i, *m.*: horse V
erro, *pp.* -atus, v.: to err, wander XV
et, conj.: and IV
externus, -a, -um, adj.: external X

F

facies, -ei, *f.*: face II
facio (-fac, -fic, -fice, *and* -fy *are variant English bases of* facio), *pp.* factus (-fect), v.: to do, build, make I
falx, falcis, *f.*: sickle, scythe IX
fascis, -is, *m.*: bundle IV
febris, -is, *f.*: fever II
felis, -is, *f.*: cat XV
femur, -oris, *or* -inis, *n.*: thigh II
fenestra, -ae, *f.*: window II
fero, *pp.* latus, v.: to bear, carry I
ferrum, -i, *n.*: iron XV
fetus, -us, *m.*: offspring XII
fibra, -ae, *f.*: fiber V
fibula, -ae, *f.*: clasp, pin, buckle IX
figo, *pp.* fixus, v.: to fasten II
filum, -i, *n.*: thread V
fimbria, -ae, *f.*: fringe, border, XV
findo, *pp.* fissus, v.: to split, divide VI

fistula, -ae, *f.*: pipe, tube I
flagellum, -i, *n.*: whip XIV
flamma, -ae, *f.*: flame XV
flecto, *pp.* **flexus,** v.: to bend III
flo, *pp.* **flatus,** v.: to blow I
floccus, -i, *m.*: tuft of wool IX
fluo, *pp.* **fluxus,** v.: to flow II
folium, -i, *n.*: leaf XII
foramen, -inis, *n.*: aperture II
forma, -ae, *f.*: form III
foro, *pp.* **-atus,** v.: to bore VI
fortis, -e, adj.: strong XIII
fossa, -ae, *f.*: ditch, trench II
fovea, -ae, *f.*: pit II
frango, *pp.* **fractus,** v.: to break V
frenum, -i, *n.*: bridle, reins, bit XIV
frons, frontis, *f.*: forehead, front V
frux, frugis, *f.*: fruit XIII
fugo, *pp.* **-atus,** v.: to put to flight XVI
fundo, *pp.* **fusus,** v.: to pour III
fungor, *pp.* **functus,** v.: to perform,
serve XVI
fungus, -i, *m.*: mushroom, fungus
XIV
funis, -is, *m.*: cord, rope I
furca, -ae, *f.*: fork VII

G

genero, *pp.* **-atus,** v.: to beget XIV
genu, pl. **genua,** *n.*: knee V
germen, -inis, *n.*: sprout, bud, germ
XV
gero, *pp.* **gestus,** v.: to bear VII
gibbus, -i, *m.*: hump XV
gingiva, -ae, *f.*: gum X
glans, glandis, *f.*: acorn XVI
glomus, -eris, *n.*: skein, clew III
gradior, *pp.* **gressus,** v.: to step, walk
XVI
granum, -i, *n.*: a grain, seed XVI
grex gregis, *m.*: flock, herd XIV
gusto, *pp.* **-atus,** v.: to taste VI
guttur, -uris, *n.*: throat IX
gyrus, -i, *m.*: circle IX

H

hallux, -ucis, *m.*: great toe XIII
halo, *pp.* **-atus,** v.: to breathe XV
hamus, -i, *m.*: hook XIII
herba, -ae, *f.*: herb VI
heres, heredis, *c.*: an heir XVI
hernia, -ae, *f.*: rupture VII
hora, -ae, *f.*: hour VII
hospes, -itis, *m.* or *f.*: guest, host V
humerus, -i, *m.*: shoulder IV

I

ilium, -i, *n.*: hipbone IV
immunis, -e, adj.: free from service
XVI
indico, *pp.* **-atus,** v.: to point out VI
infans, -ntis, *m.* or *f.*: infant IX
inferior, -oris, comp. adj.: below,
lower II
inguen, -inis, *n.*: groin IV
internus, -a, -um, adj.: inner X
intestinum, -i, *n.*: intestines, guts,
bowels XII

J

jacio, *pp.* **jactus, (-ject),** v.: to throw
IV
jaculum, -i, *n.* dart XII
jecur, -oris, *n.*: liver XII
jugulum, -i, *n.*: throat, neck XII
jungo, *pp.* **junctus,** v.: to join, unite,
connect V

L

labium, -i, *n.*: lip V
lac, lactis, *n.*: milk I
lacrima, -ae, *f.*: tear II
lacto, *pp.* **-atus,** v.: to suckle II
lamina, -ae, *f.*: thin plate, flat layer X
latus, -eris, *n.*: side I
laxo, *pp.* **-atus,** v.: to loosen V
lenis, -e, adj.: gentle, mild V
lens, lentis, *f.*: lentil (lens) III
levigo, *pp.* **-atus,** v.: to make smooth X
lignum, -i, *n.*: wood VI

ligo, *pp.* -atus, v.: to bind, tie IV
lingua, -ae, *f.*: tongue I
lino, *pp.* litus, v.: to smear upon X
lobus, -i, *m.*: lobe of the ear VI
loco, *pp.* -atus, v.: to place IV
locus, -i, *m.*: place IV
longissimus, -a, -um, sup. adj.: longest IV
longus, -a, -um, adj.: long IV
lumbricus, -i, *m.*: worm X
lumbus, -i, *m.*: loin IV
lumen, -inis, *n.*: light X
luna, -ae, *f.*: moon III
lupus, -i, *m.*: wolf VI
lux, lucis, *f.*: light XVI
lympha, -ae, *f.*: clear spring water XV

M

macero, *pp.* -atus, v.: to soften, soak V
macula, -ae, *f.*: spot XIV
magnus, -a, -um, adj.: great, large XIV
major, -oris, comp. adj.: greater X
mala, -ae, *f.*: cheek, cheekbone II
male, adv.: badly, ill I
mamma, -ae, *f.*: breast V
manus, -us, *f.*: hand IV
mater, matris, *f.*: mother XIII
maturo, *pp.* -atus, v.: to ripen X
maxilla, -ae, *f.*: jawbone VI
maximus, -a, -um, sup. adj.: greatest VI
meatus, -us, *m.*: going, passage, course III
medicus, -a, -um, adj.: pertaining to healing IV
medius, -a, -um, adj.: middle IV
medulla, -ae, *f.* marrow XI
mel, mellis, *n.* honey V
membrana, -ae, *f.*: skin IX
mens, mentis, *f.*: mind V
mensis, -is, *m.*: month V
mentum, -i, *n.*: chin V
mille, num.: one thousand VII

minor, -oris, comp. adj.: lesser X
misceo, *pp.* mixtus, v.: to mix II
mitigo, *pp.* -atus, v.: to make soft XIV
mitto, *pp.* missus, v.: to send XIV
moles, -is, *f.*: mass XV
mollis, -e, adj.: soft XIV
moneo, *pp.* monitus, v.: to warn X
morbus, -i, *m.*: disease, sickness I
mors, mortis, *f.*: death XI
moveo, *pp.* motus, v.: to move VI
mucus, -i, *m.*: mucous matter of nose XIII
murus, -i, *m.*: wall X
mus, muris, *m.* or *f.*: mouse X
musca, -ae, *f.*: fly XIII
musculus, -i, *m.*: muscle X
muto, *pp.* -atus, v.: to change XIII

N

naris, -is, *f.*: nostril XIII
nascor, *pp.* natus, v.: to be born XIII
nasus, -i, *m.*: nose II
navis, -is, *f.*: ship XIII
nebula, -ae, *f.*: cloud, fog, mist XIII
nervus, -i, *m.*: nerve VII
nevus, -i, *m.*: birthmark XIII
nidus, -i, *m.*: nest XIII
niger, -ra, -rum, adj.: black VII
nodus, -i, *m.*: knot XIII
nonus, -a, -um, adj.: ninth VII
norma, -ae, *f.*: rule, pattern VII
novem, num.: nine VII
nox, noctis, *f.*: night XI
nucleus, -i, *m.*: kernel or inside of anything XI
nuntius (nuncius), -i, *m.*: messenger III
nutrio, *pp.* nutritus, v.: to feed, nourish XIII

O

occiput, -itis, *n.*: back of the head I
occulo, *pp.* occultus, v.: to hide, cover, XV
octavus, -a, -um, adj.: eighth VII

octo, num.: eight VII
oculus, -i, *m.*: eye II
odor, -oris, *m.*: scent, smell, odor XIII
oleum, -i, *n.*: oil VII
omnis, -e, adj.: all, every VII
operor, *pp.* **-atus,** v.: to work X
orbis, -is, *m.*: a circle XVI
os, oris, *n.*: mouth II
os, ossis, *n.*: bone V
ostium, -i, *n.*: door, entrance, opening XIV
ovum, -i, *n.*: egg III

P

palatum, -i, *n.*: palate XI
palpebra, -ae, *f.*: eyelid II
palpo, *pp.* **-atus,** v.: to touch gently XV
pannus, -i, *m.*: cloth III
papilla, -ae, *f.*: nipple; dim. of *papula*, pimple I
paries, -etis, *m.*: wall II
pario, *pp.* **paritus** *or* **partus,** v.: to bear III
paro, *pp.* **-atus,** v.: to prepare, get ready X
pars, partis, *f.*: part III
parturio, *pp.* **parturitus,** v.: to be in labor III
partus, -us, *m.*: birth II
pectus, -oris, *n.*: breast, breastbone IX
pediculus, -i, *m.*: louse XIII
pello, *pp.* **pulsus,** v.: to beat, drive XIII
pelvis, -is, *f.*: basin IX
pendeo, *pp.* **pensus,** v.: to hang down XVI
penis, ,-is, *m.*: male organ of copulation XI
penna, -ae, *f.*: feather XIII
persona, -ae, *f.*: mask XVI
pes, pedis, *m.*: foot IX
petra, -ae, *f.*: rock, stone IX
pilo, *pp.* **-atus,** v.: to plunder, heap to-gether XVI
pilus, -i, *m.*: hair XI
pituita, -ae, *f.*: phlegm, rheum XVI
pius, -a, -um, adj.: pious, gentle, tender XIII
placenta, -ae, *f.*: flat cake XII
planto, *pp.* **-atus,** v.: to plant XVI
pleo, *pp.* **pletus,** v.: to fill XIV
plexus, -us, *m.*: braid, plaiting XII
plica, -ae, *f.*: fold, plait XII
plico, *pp.* **-atus,** v.: to fold V
pluma, -ae, *f.*: feather V
plumbum, -i, *n.*: lead IX
pollex, -icis, *m.*: thumb XIII
pono, *pp.* **positus,** v.: to place V
pons, pontis, *m.*: bridge XI
porta, -ae, *f.*: gate III
posterior, -oris, comp. adj.: after (time or place), behind I
potens, -entis, adj.: powerful X
premo, *pp.* **pressus,** v.: to press III
primus, -a, -um, adj.: first VII
proximus, -a, -um, sup. adj.: next X
puber, -eris, *f.*: an adult XVI
pubes, -is, *f.*: hair on genitals, genitals XVI
pulmo, -onis, *m.*: lungs IV
pulsus, -us, *m.*: beating, stroke XIII
punctum, -i, *n.*: point, prick XIII
purus, -a, -um, adj.: pure II
pus, puris, *n.*: corrupt matter, pus III
puto, *pp.* **-atus,** v.: to reckon, calculate XVI
putris, -e, adj.: rotten XV

Q

quantus, -a, -um, adj.: how much, how many V
quartus, -a, -um, adj.: fourth VII
quater, adv.: four times VII
quattuor, num.: four VII
quinque, num.: five VII
quintus, -a, -um, adj.: fifth VII

R

radius, -i, *m.*: ray, rod IX
radix, -icis, *f.*: root V
rado, *pp.* **rasus,** v.: to scrape, rub XV
ramus, -i, *m.*: branch XI
rana, -ae, *f.*: frog XI
regio, -onis, *f.*: territory, region XI
rego, *pp.* **rectus,** v.: to straighten, guide, direct XI
regula, -ae, *f.*: rule, stick XIII
ren, renis, *m.*: kidney III
rete, -is, *n.*: net III
rigidus, -a, -um, adj.: stiff, unbending, rigid XIII
rostrum, -i, *n.*: beak III
ruber, -bra, -brum, adj.: red III
rumpo, *pp.* **ruptus,** v.: to break, burst V

S

sacer, -cra, -crum, adj.: sacred, holy V
sagitta, -ae, *f.*: arrow III
sanguis, -inis, *m.*: blood II
sanus, -a, -um, adj.: sound, healthy, sane XIV
scapula, -ae, *f.*: shoulder blade IV
scindo, *pp.* **scissus,** v.: to cut, tear, split VI
scribo, *pp.* **scriptus,** v.: to write IV
scrotum, -i, *n.*: bag, scrotum XI
scutum, -i, *n.*: shield XIII
sebum, -i, *n.*: grease, fat, tallow XIV
seco, *pp.* **sectus,** v.: to cut XII
secundus, -a, -um, adj.: second VII
semen, -inis, *n.*: seed XIII
septem, num.: seven VII
septimus, -a, -um, adj.: seventh VII
septum, -i, *n.*: partition, enclosure XV
servo, *pp.* **-atus,** v.: to save, keep V
seta, -ae, *f.*: bristle VI
sex, num.: six VII
sextus, -a, -um, adj.: sixth VII
signo, *pp.* **-atus,** v.: to set a mark upon, write IV

signum, -i, *n.*: mark, sign IV
sinister, -tra, -trum, adj.: left III
sinus, -us, *m.*: a fold, cavity XVI
sol, solis, *m.* sun V
solvo, *pp.* **solutus,** v.: to set free, loosen III
somnus, -i, *m.*: sleep I
sopor, -oris, *m.*: deep sleep XV
soror, -oris, *f.*: sister XV
spargo, *pp.* **sparsus,** v.: to scatter XVI
spatium, -i, *n.*: space, room, interval XII
spicio, *pp.* **spectus,** v.: to look, see IV
spina, -ae, *f.*: thorn, spine, backbone IV
squama, -ae, *f.*: scale XII
sterilis, -e, adj.: barren, not fertile, sterile XV
sternum, -i, *n.*: chest III
sto (stat), v.: to stand X
stratum, -i, *n.*: covering XII
stria, -ae, *f.*: channel, ridge, furrow XIV
strio, *pp.* **-atus,** v.: to striate, flute XIV
struma, -ae, *f.*: swelling, tumor XIV
sudor, -oris, *m.*: sweat I
sulcus, -i, *m.*: ditch, trench IX
superior, -oris, comp. adj.: farther above, upper I
sura, -ae, *f.*: calf of the leg V

T

talus, -i, *m.*: ankle, anklebone IX
tango, *pp.* **tactus,** v.: to touch XVI
tardus, -a, -um, adj.: slow XIII
tarsus, -i, *m.*: instep XI
tego, *pp.* **tectus,** v.: to cover VI
tempus, -oris, *n.*: time, temple of the head I
tendo, *pp.* **tentus** *or* **tensus,** v.: to stretch V
ter, adv.: three times VII
tergeo, *pp.* **tersus,** v.: to wipe II

tertius, -a, -um, adj.: third VII
testis, -is, *m.*: testicle XI
tibia, -ae, *f.*: shinbone IX
tolero, *pp.* -atus, v.: to bear, endure IV
totus, -a, -um, adj.: all X
traho, *pp.* tractus, v.: to draw I
tres, tria, adj.: three VII
trochlea, -ae, *f.*: pulley XV
truncus, -i, *m.*: stem, trunk XI
tuber, -eris, *n.*: swelling XII
tubus, -i, *m.*: pipe, tube XII
tussis, -is, *f.*: cough XI

U

uber, -eris, adj.: fertile, fruitful, copious XIV
ulcus, -eris, *n.*: sore, ulcer X
ulna, -ae, *f.*: elbow, arm IV
uncus, -i, *m.*: hook XII
unguis, -is, *m.*: nail XI
unus, -a, -um, adj.: one VII
urina, -ae, *f.*: urine VI
urtica, -ae, *f.*: nettle XIV
uterus, -i, *m.*: womb XI
uva, -ae, *f.*: grape IX

V

vacca, -ae, *f.*: cow IX
vacuus, -a, -um, adj.: empty XIII

vagina, -ae, *f.*: sheath, vagina XI
vas, vasis, *n.*: vessel VI
veho, *pp.* vectus, v.: to carry, bear, draw VII
velum, -i, *n.*: veil, sail VI
vena, -ae, *f.*: vein VI
venter, -tris, *m.*: belly III
vermis, -is, *m.*: worm, grub XVI
vertebra, -ae, *f.*: joint, vertebra of the spine IX
vertex, -icis, *m.*: whirl XVI
verto (vorto), *pp.* versus, v.: to turn IX
verus, -a, -um, adj.: true IV
vesica, -ae, *f.* bladder IV
video, *pp.* visus, v.: to see X
vir, -i, *m.*: man IV
virus, -i, *n.*: poison V
viscus, -eris, *n.*: internal organs IV
vita, -ae, *f.*: life XVI
vitreus, -a, -um, adj.: glassy X
vitrum, -i, *n.*: glass X
vivus, -a, -um, adj.: living, alive XII
vomer, vomeris, *m.*: ploughshare XII
voro, *pp.* voratus, v.: to devour, eat VI
vulnus, -eris, *n.*: wound XIV
vulva, -ae, *f.*: womb XII

ENGLISH-LATIN VOCABULARY

A

acorn: glans, glandis, *f.*
adult: puber, -eris, *f.*
after (time or place) (behind): posterior, -oris, comp. adj.
all (every): omnis, -e, adj.
all: totus, -a, -um, adj.
ankle (anklebone): talus, -i, *m.*
aperture: foramen, -inis, *n.*
armpit: axilla, -ae, *f.*
arrow: sagitta, -ae, *f.*

B

back: dorsum, -i, *n.*
back of the head: occiput, -itis, *n.*
badly (ill): male, adv.
bag (scrotum): scrotum, -i, *n.*
bark (outer layer): cortex, -icis, *m.*
barren (not fertile, sterile): sterilis, -e, adj.
basin: pelvis, -is, *f.*
beak: rostrum, -i, *n.*
bear (carry): fero, *pp.* latus, v.
bear: gero, *pp.* gestus, v.
bear (produce): pario, *pp.* paritus *or* partus, v.
bear (endure): tolero, *pp.* -atus, v.
beard: barba, -ae, *f.*
beat (drive): pello, *pp.* pulsus, v.
beating (stroke): pulsus, -us, *m.*
before (time or place): anterior, -oris, comp. adj.
beget: genero, *pp.* -atus, v.
belly: abdomen, -inis, *n.*

belly: venter, -tris, *m.*
below (lower): inferior, -oris, comp. adj.
bend: flecto, *pp.* flexus, v.
berry: bacca, -ae, *f.*
bile: bilis, -is, *f.*
bind (tie): ligo, *pp.* -atus, v.
birth: partus, -us, *m.*
birthmark: nevus, -i, *m.*
black: niger, -ra, -rum, adj.
bladder: vesica, -ae, *f.*
blood: sanguis, -inis, *m.*
blow: flo, *pp.* flatus, v.
body (mass): corpus, -oris, *n.*
boil: coquo, *pp.* coctus, v.
bone: os, ossis, *n.*
bore: foro, *pp.* -atus, v.
born, to be: nascor, *pp.* natus, v.
boy: puer, pueri, *m.*
braid (plaiting): plexus, -us, *m.*
brain: cerebrum, -i, *n.*
branch: ramus, -i, *m.*
break: frango, *pp.* fractus, v.
break (burst): rumpo, *pp.* ruptus, v.
breast: mamma, -ae, *f.*
breast (breastbone): pectus, -oris, *n.*
breathe: halo, *pp.* -atus, v.
bridge: pons, pontis, *m.*
bridle (reins, bit): frenum, -i, *n.*
bristle: seta, -ae, *f.*
bundle: fascis, -is, *m.*

C

calf of the leg: sura, -ae, *f.*
care of, to take (see to): curo, *pp.*

181

-atus, v.

carry (bear, draw): veho, *pp.* vectus, v.

cat: felis, -is, *f.*

cavity: alveus, -i, *m.*

center (middle point): centrum, -i, *n.*

certain (sure): certus, -a, -um, adj.

change: muto, *pp.* -atus, v.

channel (ridge, furrow): stria, -ae, *f.*

cheek: bucca, -ae, *f.*

cheek (cheekbone): mala, -ae, *f.*

chest: sternum, -i, *n.*

chin: mentum, -i, *n.*

circle: circus, -i, *m.*

circle: gyrus, -i, *m.*

circle: orbis, -is, *m.*

clasp (pin, buckle): fibula, -ae, *f.*

close (shut): cludo, *pp.* clusus, v.

cloth: pannus, -i, *m.*

cloud (fog, mist): nebula, -ae, *f.*

club: clava, -ae, *f.*

coal: carbo, -onis, *m.*

column: columna, -ae, *f.*

cone: conus, -i, *m.*

copulation, male organ of: penis, -is, *m.*

cord (rope): funis, -is, *m.*

corrupt matter (pus): pus, puris, *n.*

cough: tussis, -is, *f.*

cover: tego, *pp.* tectus, v.

covering: stratum, -i, *n.*

cow: vacca, -ae, *f.*

crab (cancer): cancer, -cri, *m.*

crown: corona, -ae, *f.*

cultivate (to take care of): colo, *pp.* cultus, v.

cut (kill, destroy): caedo (cid), *pp.* caesus (cis), v.

cut (tear, split): scindo, *pp.* scissus, v.

cut: seco, *pp.* sectus, v.

D

dart: jaculum, -i, *n.*

day: dies, -ei, *f.*

death: mors, mortis, *f.*

deep sleep: sopor, -oris, *m.*

devour (eat): voro, *pp.* voratus, v.

disease (sickness): morbus, -i, *m.*

distribute by weight: dispenso, *pp.* -atus, v.

ditch (trench): sulcus, -i, *m.*

divide (separate): divido, *pp.* divisus, v.

do (perform, make): ago, *pp.* actus, v.

do (build, make): facio (-fac, -fic, -fice, *and* -fy *are variant English bases of* facio), *pp.* factus (-fect), v.

dog: canis, -is, *m.* or *f.*

door (entrance, opening): ostium, -i, *n.*

drain (milk out): emulgeo, *pp.* emulsus, v.

draw (lead): duco, *pp.* ductus, v.

draw: traho, *pp.* tractus, v.

duct (canal): ductus, -us, *m.*

E

ear: auris, -is, *f.*

egg: ovum, -i, *n.*

eight: octo, num.

eighth: octavus, -a, -um, adj.

elbow: cubitum, -i, *n.*

elbow (arm): ulna, -ae, *f.*

empty: vacuus, -a, -um, adj.

err (wander): erro, *pp.* -atus, v.

external: externus, -a, -um, adj.

eye: oculus, -i, *m.*

eyelid: cilium, -i, *n.*

eyelid: palpebra, -ae, *f.*

F

face: facies, -ei, *f.*

farther above (upper): superior, -oris, comp. adj.

fasten: figo, *pp.* fixus, v.

fat: adeps, adipis, *m.* or *f.*

feather: penna, -ae, *f.*

feather: pluma, -ae, *f.*

feed (nourish): nutrio, *pp.* nutritus, v.

fertile (fruitful, copious): uber, -eris, adj.
fever: febris, -is, *f.*
fiber: fibra, -ae, *f.*
fifth: quintus, -a, -um,, adj.
fill: pleo, *pp.* pletus, v.
finger (toe): digitus, -i, *m.*
first: primus, -a, -um, adj.
five: quinque, num.
flame: flamma, -ae, *f.*
flat cake: placenta, -ae, *f.*
flight, put to: fugo, *pp.* -atus, v.
flock (herd): grex, gregis, *m.*
flow: fluo, *pp.* fluxus, v.
fly: musca, -ae, *f.*
fold (plait): plica, -ae, *f.*
fold: plico, *pp.* -atus, v.
fold (cavity): sinus, -us, *m.*
food: cibus, -i, *m.*
foot: pes, pedis, *m.*
forehead (front): frons, frontis, *f.*
fork: furca, -ae, *f.*
form: forma, -ae, *f.*
four: quattuor, num.
fourth: quartus, -a, -um, adj.
four times: quater, adv.
free from service: immunis, -e, adj.
fringe (border): fimbria, -ae, *f.*
frog: rana, -ae, *f.*
fruit: frux, frugis, *f.*

G

gate: porta, -ae, *f.*
gentle (mild): lenis, -e, adj.
glass: vitrum, -i, *n.*
glassy: vitreus, -a, -um, adj.
go: cedo, *pp.* cessus, v.
going (passage, course): meatus, -us, *m.*
grain (seed): granum, -i, *n.*
grape: uva, -ae, *f.*
grease (fat, tallow): sebum, -i, *n.*
great (large): magnus, -a, -um, adj.
greater: major, -oris, comp. adj.

great toe: hallux, -ucis, *m.*
gristle (cartilage): cartilago, -inis, *f.*
groin: inguen, -inis, *n.*
grow: cresco, *pp.* cretus, v.
guest (host): hospes, -itis, *m.* or *f.*
gum: gingiva, -ae, *f.*

H

hair: pilus, -i, *m.*
hair on genitals (genitals): pubes, -is, *f.*
hand: manus, -us, *f.*
hang down: pendeo, *pp.* pensus, v.
hard: durus, -a, -um, adj.
harden: duro, *pp.* -atus, v.
hard skin: callus, -i, *m.*
head: caput, -itis, *n.*
healing, pertaining to: medicus, -a, -um, adj.
heart: cor, cordis, *n.*
heat: calor, -oris, *m.*
heir: heres, heredis, *c.*
herb: herba, -ae, *f.*
hide (cover): occulo, *pp.* occultus, v.
hill: collis, -is, *m.*
hip (hip joint): coxa, -ae, *f.*
hipbone: ilium -i, *n.*
hollow (concave): cavus, -a, -um, adj.
honey: mel, mellis, *n.*
hook: hamus, -i, *m.*
hook: uncus, -i, *m.*
horn: cornu, -us, *n.*
horse: equus, -i, *m.*
hour: hora, -ae, *f.*
how much (how many): quantus, -a, -um, adj.
hump: gibbus, -i, *m.*
hundred: centum, num.

I

infant: infans, -ntis, *m.* or *f.*
inner: internus, -a, -um, adj.
instep: tarsus, -i, *m.*
internal organs: viscus, -eris, *n.*
intestines (guts, bowels): intestinum,

-i, *n.*
iron: ferrum, -i, *n.*

J

jawbone: maxilla, -ae, *f.*
join (unite, connect): jungo, *pp.* junctus, v.
joint (vertebra of the spine): vertebra, -ae, *f.*

K

kernel (inside of anything): nucleus, -i, *m.*
key: clavis, -is, *f.*
kidney: ren, renis, *m.*
knee: genu, *pl.* genua, *n.*
knot: nodus, -i, *m.*

L

labor, to be in: parturio, *pp.* parturitus, v.
lead: plumbum, -i, *n.*
leaf: folium, -i, *n.*
lentil (lens): lens, lentis, *f.*
lesser: minor, -oris, comp. adj.
lie in bed: cubo (cubit), v.
life: vita, -ae, *f.*
light: lumen, inis, *n.*
light: lux, lucis, *f.*
limestone: calx, calcis, *f.*
limp: claudico, *pp.* -atus, v.
lip: labium, -i, *n.*
listen to: ausculto, *pp.* -atus, v.
liver: jecur, -oris, *n.*
living (alive): vivus, -a, -um, adj.
lobe of the ear: lobus, -i, *m.*
loin: lumbus, -i, *m.*
long: longus, -a, -um, adj.
longest: longissimus, -a, -um, sup. adj.
look (see): spicio, *pp.* spectus, v.
loosen: laxo, *pp.* -atus, v.
louse: pediculus, -i, *m.*
lungs: pulmo, -onis, *m.*

M

man: vir, -i, *m.*

mark (sign): signum, -i, *n.*
marrow: medulla, -ae, *f.*
mask: persona, -ae, *f.*
mass: moles, -is, *f.*
messenger: nuntius (nuncius), -i, *m.*
middle: medius, -a, -um, adj.
milk: lac, lactis, *n.*
mind: mens, mentis, *f.*
mix: misceo, *pp.* mixtus, v.
month: mensis, -is, *m.*
moon: luna, -ae, *f.*
mother: mater, matris, *f.*
mouse: mus, muris, *m.* or *f.*
mouth: os, -oris, *n.*
move: moveo, *pp.* motus, v.
mucous matter of nose: mucus, -i, *m.*
muscle: musculus, -i, *m.*
mushroom (fungus): fungus, -i, *m.*

N

nail: unguis, -is, *m.*
neck: cervix, -icis, *f.*
neck: collum, -i, *n.*
nerve: nervus, -i, *m.*
nest: nidus, -i, *m.*
net: rete, -is, *n.*
nettle: urtica, -ae, *f.*
next: proximus, -a, -um, sup. adj.
night: nox, noctis, *f.*
nine: novem, num.
ninth: nonus, -a, -um, adj.
nose: nasus, -i, *m.*
nostril: naris, -is, *f.*
nourish: alo, *pp.* alitus, *or* altus, v.

O

offspring: fetus, -us, *m.*
oil: oleum, -i, *n.*
one: unus, -a, -um, adj.

P

pain: dolor, -oris, *m.*
palate: palatum, -i, *n.*
part: pars, partis, *f.*
partition (enclosure): septum, -i, *n.*

perform (serve): fungor, *pp.* functus, v.

phlegm (rheum): pituita, -ae, *f.*

pious (gentle, tender): pius, -a, -um, adj.

pipe (tube): fistula, -ae, *f.*

pipe (tube): tubus, -i, *m.*

pit: fovea, -ae, *f.*

place: loco, *pp.* locatus, v.

place: locus, -i, *m.*

place: pono, *pp.* positus, v.

plant: planto, *pp.* -atus, v.

plant bulb: bulbus, -i, *m.*

plenty: copia, -ae, *f.*

ploughshare: vomer, vomeris, *m.*

plunder (heap together): pilo, *pp.* -atus, v.

point: cuspis, -idis, *f.*

point (prick): punctum, -i, *n.*

point out: indico, *pp.* -atus, v.

pour: fundo, *pp.* fusus, v.

powerful: potens, -entis, adj.

prepare (get ready): paro, *pp.* -atus, v.

press: premo, *pp.* pressus, v.

pulley: trochlea, -ae, *f.*

pure: purus, -a, -um, adj.

purse (sac): bursa, -ae, *f.*

Q

quinsy: angina, -ae, *f.*

R

ray (rod): radius, -i, *m.*

reckon (calculate): puto, *pp.* -atus, v.

rib: costa, -ae, *f.*

right: dexter, -tra, -trum, adj.

ripen: maturo, *pp.* -atus, v.

rock (stone): petra, -ae, *f.*

rod: bacillus, -i, *m.*

root: radix, -icis, *f.*

rotten: putris, -e, adj.

rule (pattern): norma, -ae, *f.*

rule (stick): regula, -ae, *f.*

run: curro, *pp.* cursus, v.

rupture: hernia, -ae, *f.*

S

sacred (holy): sacer, -cra, -crum, adj.

save (keep): servo, *pp.* -atus, v.

scale: squama, -ae, *f.*

scatter: spargo, *pp.* sparsus, v.

scent (smell, odor): odor, -oris, *m.*

scrape (rub): rado, *pp.* rasus, v.

seam (joining together): commissura, -ae, *f.*

second: secundus, -a, -um, adj.

see:: video, *pp.* visus, v.

seed: semen, -inis, *n.*

send: mitto, *pp.* missus, v.

set a mark upon (write): signo, *pp.* -atus, v.

set free (loosen): solvo, *pp.* solutus, v.

seven: septum, num.

seventh: septimus, -a, -um, adj.

sewer: cloaca, -ae, *f.*

sharp (pointed, cutting): acer, acris, acre, adj.

sheath (vagina): vagina, -ae, *f.*

shield: scutum, -i, *n.*

shinbone: tibia, -ae, *f.*

ship: navis, -is, *f.*

short: brevis, -e, adj.

shoulder: humerus, -i, *m.*

shoulder blade: scapula, -ae, *f.*

sickle (scythe): falx, falcis, *f.*

side: latus, -eris, *n.*

silver: argentum, -i, *n.*

sister: soror, -oris, *f.*

six: six, num.

sixth: sextus, -a, -um, adj.

skein (clew): glomus, -eris, *n.*

skin: cutis, -is, *f.*

skin: membrana, -ae, *f.*

sleep: somnus, -i, *m.*

slow: tardus, -a, -um, adj.

smear upon: lino, *pp.* litus, v.

smooth, to make: levigo, *pp.* -atus, v.

soft: mollis, -e, adj.

soften (soak): macero, *pp.* -atus, v.
soften: mitigo, *pp.*-atus, v.
sore (ulcer): ulcus, -eris, *n.*
sound (healthy, sane): sanus, -a, -um, adj.
sour: acidus, -a, -um, adj.
space (room, interval): spatium, -i, *n.*
speak (say): dico, *pp.* dictus, v.
split (divide): findo, *pp.* fissus, v.
spot: macula, -ae, *f.*
sprout (bud, germ): germen, -inis, *n.*
stand: sto (stat), v.
stem (trunk): truncus, -i, *m.*
step (walk): gradior, *pp.* gressus
stiff (unbending, rigid): rigidus, -a, -um, adj.
storehouse (room): cella, -ae, *f.*
straighten (guide, direct): rego, *pp.* rectus, v.
stretch: tendo, *pp.* tentus, *or* tensus, v.
striate (flute): strio, *pp.* -atus, v.
strong: fortis, -e, adj.
suckle: lacto, *pp.* -atus, v.
sun: sol, solis, *m.*
sweat: sudor, -oris, *m.*
sweet: dulcis, -e, adj.
swelling (tumor): struma, -ae, *f.*
swelling: tuber, -eris, *n.*
sword: ensis, -is, *m.*

T

tail: cauda, -ae, *f.*
take (seize): capio (cipi), *pp.* captus (cept), v.
teach (instruct): doceo, *pp.* doctus, v.
tear: lacrima, ,-ae, *f.*
ten: decem, num.
tenth: decimus, -a, -um, adj.
territory (region): regio, -onis, *f.*
testicle: testis, -is, *m.*
thin plate (flat layer): lamina, -ae, *f.*
third: tertius, -a, -um, adj.
thousand: mille, num.
thread: filum, -i, *n.*

three: tres, tria, adj.
three times: ter, adv.
throat: guttur, -uris, *n.*
throat (neck): jugulum, -i, *n.*
throw: jacio, *pp.* jactus, (-ject), v.
thumb: pollex, -icis, *m.*
time (temple of the head): tempus, -oris, *n.*
tongue: lingua, -ae, *f.*
tooth: dens, dentis, *m.*
touch: tango, *pp.* tactus, v.
touch gently: palpo, *pp.* -atus, v.
tree: arbor, -oris, *f.*
true: verus, -a, -um, adj.
tuft of wool: floccus, -i, *m.*
turn: verto (vorto), *pp.* versus, v.
twice: bis (bi-), adv.
two: duo, duae, duo, num.
two by two: bini, -ae, -a, adj.

U

unmarried (single): caelebs, -libis, adj.
urine: urina, -ae, *f.*

V

veil (sail): velum, -i, *n.*
vein: vena, -ae, *f.*
vessel: vas, vasis, *n.*
vinegar: acetum, -i, *n.*

W

walk: ambulo, *pp.* -atus, v.
wall: murus, -i, *m.*
wall: paries, -etis, *m.*
warn: moneo, *pp.* monitus, v.
water: aqua, -ae, *f.*
water, clear spring: lympha, -ae, *f.*
wax: cera, -ae, *f.*
wedge: cuneus, -i, *m.*
well: bene, adv.
whip: flagellum, -i, *n.*
whirl: vertex, -icis, *m.*
white: albus, -a, -um, adj.
window: fenestra, -ae, *f.*

wipe: tergeo, *pp.* tersus, v.
wolf: lupus, -i, *m.*
womb: uterus, -i, *m.*
womb: vulva, -ae, *f.*
wood: lignum, -i, *n.*
work: operor, *pp.* -atus, v.

worm: lumbricus, -i, *m.*
worm (grub): vermis, -is, *m.*
worthy: dignus, -a, -um, adj.
wound: vulnus, -eris, *n.*
wrist: carpus, -i, *m.*

Latin Prefixes and Suffixes

PREFIXES

Prefixes	*Meaning*
ab-, a-, abs-	from, away from
*ad-	to, toward, near
ambi-, amb-, ambo-	around, on both sides
ante-	before, in front of
antero-	before, prior
circum-	around
com-, co-, col-, con-, cor-	with, together
contra-	against, opposite
de-	down, from, away
dis-, di-, dif-	apart, not
ex-, e-, ef-	out, out of, from
extra-	beyond, outside
in-, im-, ir-	in, into, upon
in-, il-, im-, ir-	not
infra-	below, under
inter-	between, among
intra-, intro-	within, inside, inward
juxta-	near, next to
non-	not
ob-, o-, oc-, of-, op-	before, against
per-	through, throughout
post-	behind, after
postero-	behind
prae-, pre-	before, ahead
pro-	before, in front of, forward
re-, red-	back, again
retro-	backward, behind
se-	apart, without
semi-	half
sub-, suc-, suf-, sup-, sus-	under, less than, deficient
super-, supra-	over, above, excessive
trans-, tra-	across, through
ultra-	beyond, excessive

* Often assimilated to a following consonant. The adverbial suffix -*ad* also means to or toward.

SUFFIXES

English	Latin	Meaning
-able	-abilis, -e	able to be, worthy of
-ible	-ibilis, -e	
-aceous	-aceus, -a, -um	pertaining to
-acy	-acia	quality of, state, rank, office
-al	-alis, -e	pertaining or belonging to
-an	-anus, -a, -um	pertaining to
-ance	-antia	quality, condition, state, or result of
-ancy	-antia	
-ence	-entia	
-ency	-entia	
-ant	-antem	one who, that which, act or process
-ent	-entem	of
-ar	-aris, -e	pertaining to or like
-ary	-arius, -a, -um	
-ory	-orius, -a, -um	
-arium	-arium	place where
-ary	-arium	
-orium	-orium	
-ory	-orium	
-ate	-atus, -a, -um	having, provided with
-atic	-aticus, -a, -um	pertaining to
-ic	-icus, -a, -um	
-ation	-atio	act, state, condition, process, or re-
-ion	-io	sult of
-ative	-ativus, -a, -um	tending to, relating to, belonging to,
-ive	-ivus, -a, -um	or connected with
-cle	-culus, -a, -um	diminutive
-cule	-culus, -a, -um	
-icle	-iculus, -a, -um	
-ole	-olus, -a, -um	
-ule	-ulus, -a, -um	
-er		one who or that which
-or	-or	
-ety	-etas	quality, condition, or state of
-ity	-itas	
-ty	-tas	
-eous	-eus, -a, -um	belonging to or made of
-ia	-ia	quality, condition, or state of
-id	-idus, -a, -um	pertaining to
-ile	-ilis, -e	pertaining to or capable of
-il	-ilis, -e	
-ine	-inus, -a, -um	pertaining to or like

190

	Suffixes	
English	*Latin*	*Meaning*
-lent	-lentus, -a, -um	full of
-ment	-mentum	result, act, or means of
-mentum	-mentum	
-ose	-osus, -a, -um	pertaining to, having the quality of,
-ous	-osus, -a, -um	or full of
-tude	-tudo	condition, or state of
-ure	-ura	process, state, act, or result of

PHARMACEUTICAL TERMS
AND ABBREVIATIONS

Term or Phrase	Abbreviation	Meaning
absente febre	abs. feb.	fever being absent
adde; addatur	add.	add; let be added
ad libitum	ad lib.	at pleasure
admove; admoveatur	admove.	apply; let it be applied
ana	aa.	of each
ante cibos	a.c.	before meals
aqua	aq.	water
aqua destillata	aq. dest.	distilled water
bibe	bib.	drink
bis in die	b.i.d.	twice a day
capiat	cap.	let him take
capsula; capsulae	cap.	capsule; capsules
centum	C.	one hundred
charta cerata	chart. cerat.	waxed paper
cochleare amplum	coch. amp.	tablespoonful
cochleare infans	coch. inf.	teaspoonful
cum aqua	cum aq.	with water
cyathus	cyath.	a glassful
de die in diem	de d. in di.	from day to day
dentur tales doses	d.t.d.	give of such doses
dimidius	dim.	one-half (½)
dispensa; dispensetur	disp.	dispense
divide; dividatur	div.	divide
dolore urgente	dol. urg.	while pain lasts
dosis; doses	dos.	a dose; doses
drachma; drachmae	ʒ	a drachm; drachms
durante dolore	dur. dol.	while pain lasts
emplastrum	emp.	plaster
emulsum	emul.	emulsion
ex aqua	ex aq.	with water
fiat; fiant	ft.	let it be made; be made
filtra	filt.	filter

Term or Phrase	Abbreviation	Meaning
gutta; guttae	gtt.	drop; drops
hora somni	h.s.	at bedtime
illico	illic.	immediately
in aqua	in aq.	in water
in loco fervente	in loc. ferv.	in a hot place
in loco frigido	in loc. frig.	in a cold place
in vaso clauso	in vas. claus.	in a closed vessel
in vitro	in vit.	in glass
linimentum	lin.	liniment
lotio	lot.	lotion
massa	mass.	mass
misce	M.	mix
mistura	mist.	mixture
non repetatur	non rep.	do not repeat
numero	no.	number
omni die	o.d.	daily
omni mane	o.m.	every morning
omni nocte	o.n.	every night
omni secunda hora	omn. 2 hr.	every second hour
omni tertia hora	omn. tert. hr.	every third hour
pasta	past.	paste
phiala prius agitata	p.p.a.	the bottle first being shaken
pilula; pilulae	pil.	pill; pills
pone	----	place; put
post cibos	p.c.	after meals
pro re nata	p.r.n.	as the occasion arises
pro usu externo	pro us. ext.	for external use
pulvis; pulveres	pulv.	powder; powders
quantitatem sufficientem	q.s.	sufficient quantity
quater in die	q.i.d.	four times a day
recipe	R	take
signa; signetur	Sig.	write; let be written
sinapis	sinap.	mustard
sine aqua	sin. aq.	without water
si opus sit	s.o.s.	if necessary
solutio	sol.	solution
statim	stat.	immediately
suppositorium; suppositoria	suppos.	suppository; suppositories
syrupus	syr.	syrup
tabella; tabellae	tab.	tablet; tablets
talis; tales; talia	tal.	such
ter in die	t.i.d.	three times a day
trochiscus; trochisci	troch.	a lozenge; lozenges

Term or Phrase	Abbreviation	Meaning
uncia	℥	an ounce
unguentum	ungt.	ointment
ut dictum	ut dict.	as directed
utendus	utend.	to be used
vices	vic.	times